CALIFORNIA INTEGRATED

Grade 8

elevate science

AUTHORS

You're an author!

As you write in this science book, your answers and personal discoveries will be recorded for you to keep, making this book unique to you. That is why you are one of the primary authors of this book.

In the space below, print your name, school, town, and state. Then write a short autobiography that includes your interests and accomplishments.

YOUR NAME

SCHOOL

TOWN, STATE

AUTOBIOGRAPHY

Savvas Learning Company LLC, 15 East Midland Avenue, Paramus, NJ 07652

Cover: The cover shows power generating turbines in California. Fiber optics are used in the construction of the turbines. Ice crystals are found in the clouds and a honey bee is shown with a California poppy. FCVR: Tntemerson/iStock/Getty Images Plus, Rafe Swan/Getty Images, Stefan Christmann/Getty Images, Dudarev Mikhail/Shutterstock, Sumiko Scott/Getty Images; BCVR: Marinello/DigitalVision Vectors/Getty Images.

ISBN-13: 978-1-418-31042-4
ISBN-10: 1-418-31042-5
4 21

Program Authors

ZIPPORAH MILLER, Ed.D.
Coordinator for K-12 Science Programs, Anne Arundel County Public Schools
Dr. Zipporah Miller currently serves as the Senior Manager for Organizational Learning with the Anne Arundel County Public School System. Prior to that she served as the K-12 Coordinator for science in Anne Arundel County. She conducts national training to science stakeholders on the Next Generation Science Standards. Dr. Miller also served as the Associate Executive Director for Professional Development Programs and conferences at the National Science Teachers Association (NSTA) and served as a reviewer during the development of Next Generation Science Standards. Dr. Miller holds a doctoral degree from the University of Maryland College Park, a master's degree in school administration and supervision from Bowie State University and a bachelor's degree from Chadron State College.

MICHAEL J. PADILLA, Ph.D.
Professor Emeritus, Eugene P. Moore School of Education, Clemson University, Clemson, South Carolina
Michael J. Padilla taught science in middle and secondary schools, has more than 30 years of experience educating middle-school science teachers, and served as one of the writers of the 1996 U.S. National Science Education Standards. In recent years Mike has focused on teaching science to English Language Learners. His extensive experience as Principal Investigator on numerous National Science Foundation and U.S. Department of Education grants resulted in more than $35 million in funding to improve science education. He served as president of the National Science Teachers Association, the world's largest science teaching organization, in 2005–6.

MICHAEL E. WYSESSION, Ph.D
Professor of Earth and Planetary Sciences, Washington University, St. Louis, Missouri
Author of more than 100 science and science education publications, Dr. Wysession was awarded the prestigious National Science Foundation Presidential Faculty Fellowship and Packard Foundation Fellowship for his research in geophysics, primarily focused on using seismic tomography to determine the forces driving plate tectonics. Dr. Wysession is also a leader in geoscience literacy and education; he is the chair of the Earth Science Literacy Initiative, the author of several popular video lectures on geology in the *Great Courses* series, and a lead writer of the *Next Generation Science Standards**.

---

*Next Generation Science Standards is a registered trademark of WestEd. Neither WestEd nor the lead states and partners that developed the Next Generation Science Standards were involved in the production of this product, and do not endorse it. NGSS Lead States. 2013. *Next Generation Science Standards: For States, By States.* Washington, DC: The National Academies Press.

REVIEWERS

Program Consultants

Carol Baker
Science Curriculum

Dr. Carol K. Baker is superintendent for Lyons Elementary K-8 School District in Lyons, Illinois. Prior to this, she was Director of Curriculum for Science and Music in Oak Lawn, Illinois. Before this she taught Physics and Earth Science for 18 years. In the recent past, Dr. Baker also wrote assessment questions for ACT (EXPLORE and PLAN), was elected president of the Illinois Science Teachers Association from 2011–2013, and served as a member of the Museum of Science and Industry (Chicago) advisory board. She is a writer of the Next Generation Science Standards. Dr. Baker received her B.S. in Physics and a science teaching certification. She completed her master's of Educational Administration (K-12) and earned her doctorate in Educational Leadership.

Jim Cummins
ELL

Dr. Cummins's research focuses on literacy development in multilingual schools and the role technology plays in learning across the curriculum. *Elevate Science* incorporates research-based principles for integrating language with the teaching of academic content based on Dr. Cummins's work.

Elfrieda Hiebert
Literacy

Dr. Hiebert, a former primary-school teacher, is President and CEO of TextProject, a non-profit aimed at providing open-access resources for instruction of beginning and struggling readers, She is also a research associate at the University of California Santa Cruz. Her research addresses how fluency, vocabulary, and knowledge can be fostered through appropriate texts, and her contributions have been recognized through awards such as the Oscar Causey Award for Outstanding Contributions to Reading Research (Literacy Research Association, 2015), Research to Practice award (American Educational Research Association, 2013), and the William S. Gray Citation of Merit Award for Outstanding Contributions to Reading Research (International Reading Association, 2008).

Content Reviewers

Alex Blom, Ph.D.
Associate Professor
Department Of Physical Sciences
Alverno College
Milwaukee, Wisconsin

Joy Branlund, Ph.D.
Department of Physical Science
Southwestern Illinois College
Granite City, Illinois

Judy Calhoun
Associate Professor
Physical Sciences
Alverno College
Milwaukee, Wisconsin

Stefan Debbert
Associate Professor of Chemistry
Lawrence University
Appleton, Wisconsin

Diane Doser
Professor
Department of Geological Sciences
University of Texas at El Paso
El Paso, Texas

Rick Duhrkopf, Ph.D.
Department of Biology
Baylor University
Waco, Texas

Jennifer Liang
University of Minnesota Duluth
Duluth, Minnesota

Heather Mernitz, Ph.D.
Associate Professor of Physical Sciences
Alverno College
Milwaukee, Wisconsin

Joseph McCullough, Ph.D.
Cabrillo College
Aptos, California

Katie M. Nemeth, Ph.D.
Assistant Professor
College of Science and Engineering
University of Minnesota Duluth
Duluth, Minnesota

Maik Pertermann
Department of Geology
Western Wyoming Community College
Rock Springs, Wyoming

Scott Rochette
Department of the Earth Sciences
The College at Brockport State University of New York
Brockport, New York

David Schuster
Washington University in St Louis
St. Louis, Missouri

Shannon Stevenson
Department of Biology
University of Minnesota Duluth
Duluth, Minnesota

Paul Stoddard, Ph.D.
Department of Geology and Environmental Geosciences
Northern Illinois University
DeKalb, Illinois

Nancy Taylor
American Public University
Charles Town, West Virginia

Teacher Reviewers

Rita Armstrong
Los Cerritos Middle School
Thousand Oaks, California

Tyler C. Britt, Ed.S.
Curriculum & Instructional
Practice Coordinator
Raytown Quality Schools
Raytown, Missouri

Holly Bowser
Barstow High School
Barstow, California

David Budai
Coachella Valley Unified School District
Coachella, California

A. Colleen Campos
Grandview High School
Aurora, Colorado

Jodi DeRoos
Mojave River Academy
Colton, California

Colleen Duncan
Moore Middle School
Redlands, California

Nicole Hawke
Westside Elementary
Thermal, California

Margaret Henry
Lebanon Junior High School
Lebanon, Ohio

Ashley Humphrey
Riverside Preparatory Elementary
Oro Grande, California

Adrianne Kilzer
Riverside Preparatory Elementary
Oro Grande, California

Danielle King
Barstow Unified School District
Barstow, California

Kathryn Kooyman
Riverside Preparatory Elementary
Oro Grande, California

Esther Leonard M.Ed. and L.M.T.
Gifted and Talented Implementation Specialist
San Antonio Independent School District
San Antonio, Texas

Diana M. Maiorca, M.Ed.
Los Cerritos Middle School
Thousand Oaks, California

Kevin J. Maser, Ed.D.
H. Frank Carey Jr/Sr High School
Franklin Square, New York

Corey Mayle
Brogden Middle School
Durham, North Carolina

Keith McCarthy
George Washington Middle School
Wayne, New Jersey

Rudolph Patterson
Cobalt Institute of Math and Science
Victorville, California

Yolanda O. Peña
John F. Kennedy Junior High School
West Valley City, Utah

Stacey Phelps
Mojave River Academy
Oro Grande, California

Susan Pierce
Bryn Mawr Elementary
Redlands Unified School District
Redlands, California

Cristina Ramos
Mentone Elementary School
Redlands Unified School District
Mentone, California

Mary Regis
Franklin Elementary School
Redlands, California

Bryna Selig
Gaithersburg Middle School
Gaithersburg, Maryland

Pat (Patricia) Shane, Ph.D.
STEM & ELA Education Consultant
Chapel Hill, North Carolina

Elena Valencia
Coral Mountain Academy
Coachella, California

Janelle Vecchio
Mission Elementary School
Redlands, California

Brittney Wells
Riverside Preparatory Elementary
Oro Grande, California

Kristina Williams
Sequoia Middle School
Newbury Park, California

Safety Reviewers

Douglas Mandt, M.S.
Science Education Consultant
Edgewood, Washington

Juliana Textley, Ph.D.
Author, NSTA books on school science safety
Adjunct Professor
Lesley University
Cambridge, Massachusetts

California Spotlight  TOPICS 1–2
Instructional Segment 1

Hunting Asteroids in California

TOPIC **1**

Forces and Motion 8

Investigative Phenomenon How can you use models to demonstrate how the motion of an object will be affected by forces that act on it?

 MS-PS2-1, MS-PS2-2, MS-PS2-4, MS-PS3-1, MS-PS3-2, EP&CIa, EP&CIIb

HANDS-ON LABS

- **uConnect**
- **uInvestigate**
- **uDemonstrate**

TOPIC 2

Energy

Investigative Phenomenon How can you demonstrate that energy causes changes to occur?

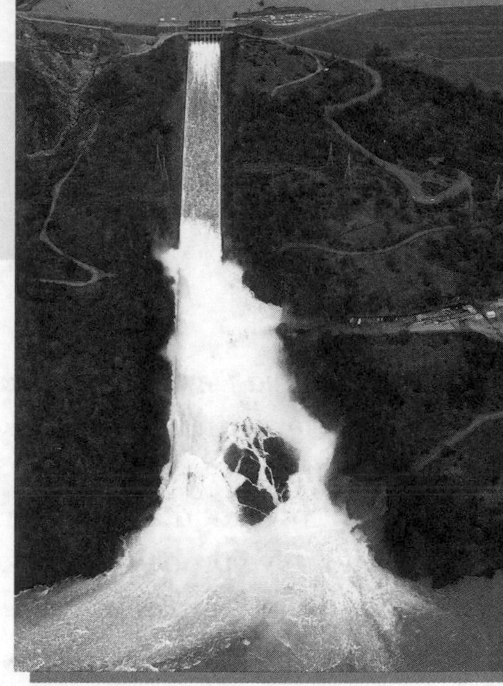

MS-PS3-1, MS-PS-3-2

uConnect

uInvestigate

uDemonstrate

Elevate your thinking!

California Elevate Science takes science to a whole new level and lets you take ownership of your learning. Explore science in the world around you. Investigate how things work. Think critically and solve problems! *California Elevate Science* helps you think like a scientist, so you're ready for a world of discoveries.

Exploring California

California spotlights explore California phenomena. Topic Quests help connect lesson concepts together and reflect 3-dimensional learning.

- Science concepts organized around phenomena
- Topics weave together 3-D learning
- Engineering focused on solving problems and improving designs

California Spotlight
Instructional Segment 2

Before the Topics

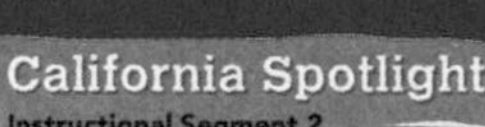

California Flood Management

Phenomenon In February of 2017, workers at the Oroville Dam were forced to use the

Student Discourse

California Elevate Science promotes active discussion, higher order thinking and analysis and prepares you for high school through:

- High-level write-in prompts
- Evidence-based arguments
- Practice in speaking and writing

Model It!

Crystalline and Amorphous Solids

Figure 5 A pat of butter is an amorphous solid. The particles that make up the butter are not arranged in a regular pattern. The sapphire gem stones are crystalline solids. Draw what you think the particles look like in a crystalline solid.

READING CHECK **Explain** In your own words, explain the main differences between crystalline solids and amorphous solids.

Quest CHECK-IN

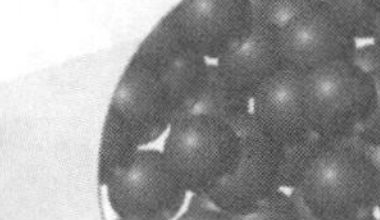

In this lesson, you learned what happens to the particles of substances during melting, freezing, evaporation, boiling, condensation, and sublimation. You also thought about how thermal energy plays a role in these changes of state.

Predict Why do you need to take the temperature of the surroundings into consideration when designing a system with materials that can change state?

Academic Vocabulary

In orange juice, bits of pulp are suspended in liquid. Explain what you think *suspended* means.

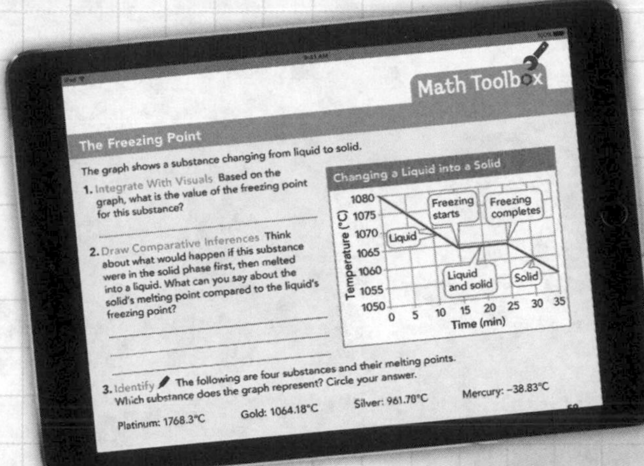

Build Literacy Skills

By connecting science to other disciplines like:

- Mathematics
- Reading and Writing
- STEM/Engineering

Focus on Inquiry

Case studies put you in the shoes of a scientist to solve real-world mysteries using real data. You will be able to:

- Analyze data
- Formulate claims
- Build evidence-based arguments

Enter the Digital Classroom

Virtual labs, 3-D expeditions, and dynamic videos take science beyond the classroom.

- Open-ended virtual labs
- Google Expeditions and field trips
- NBC Learn videos

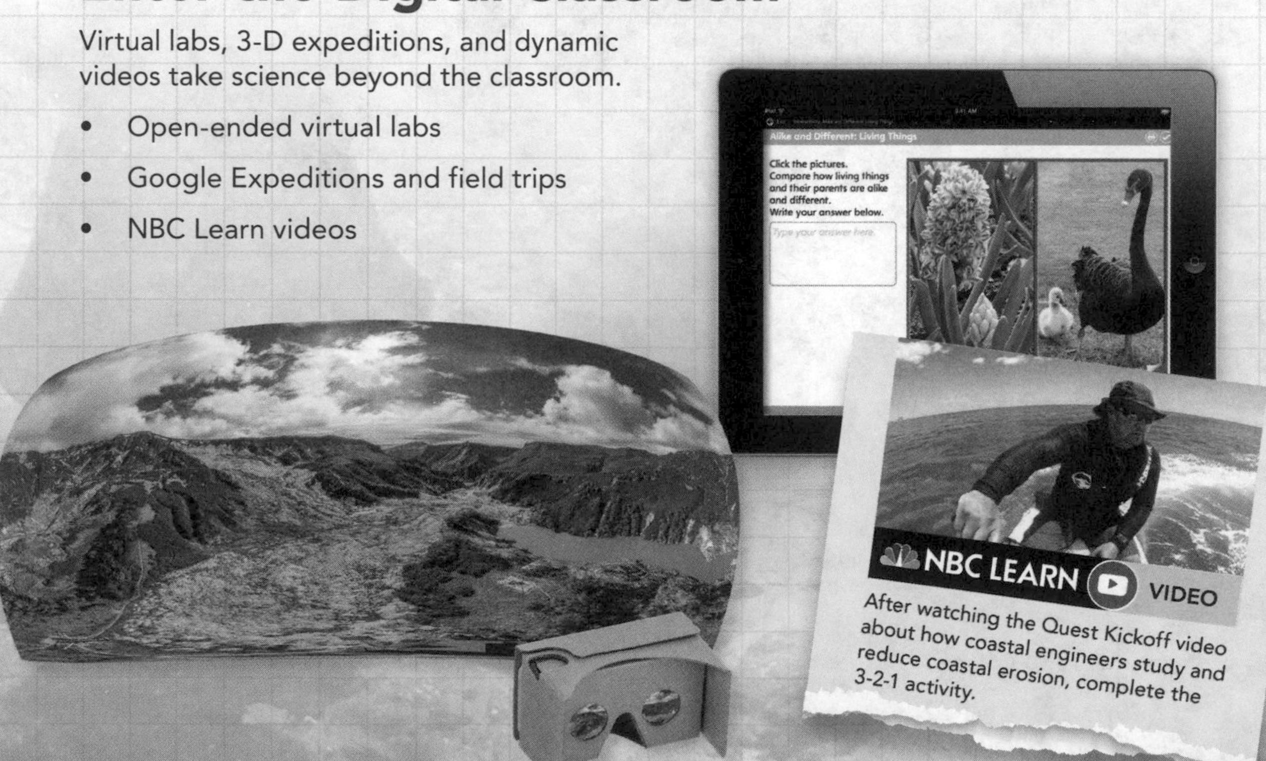

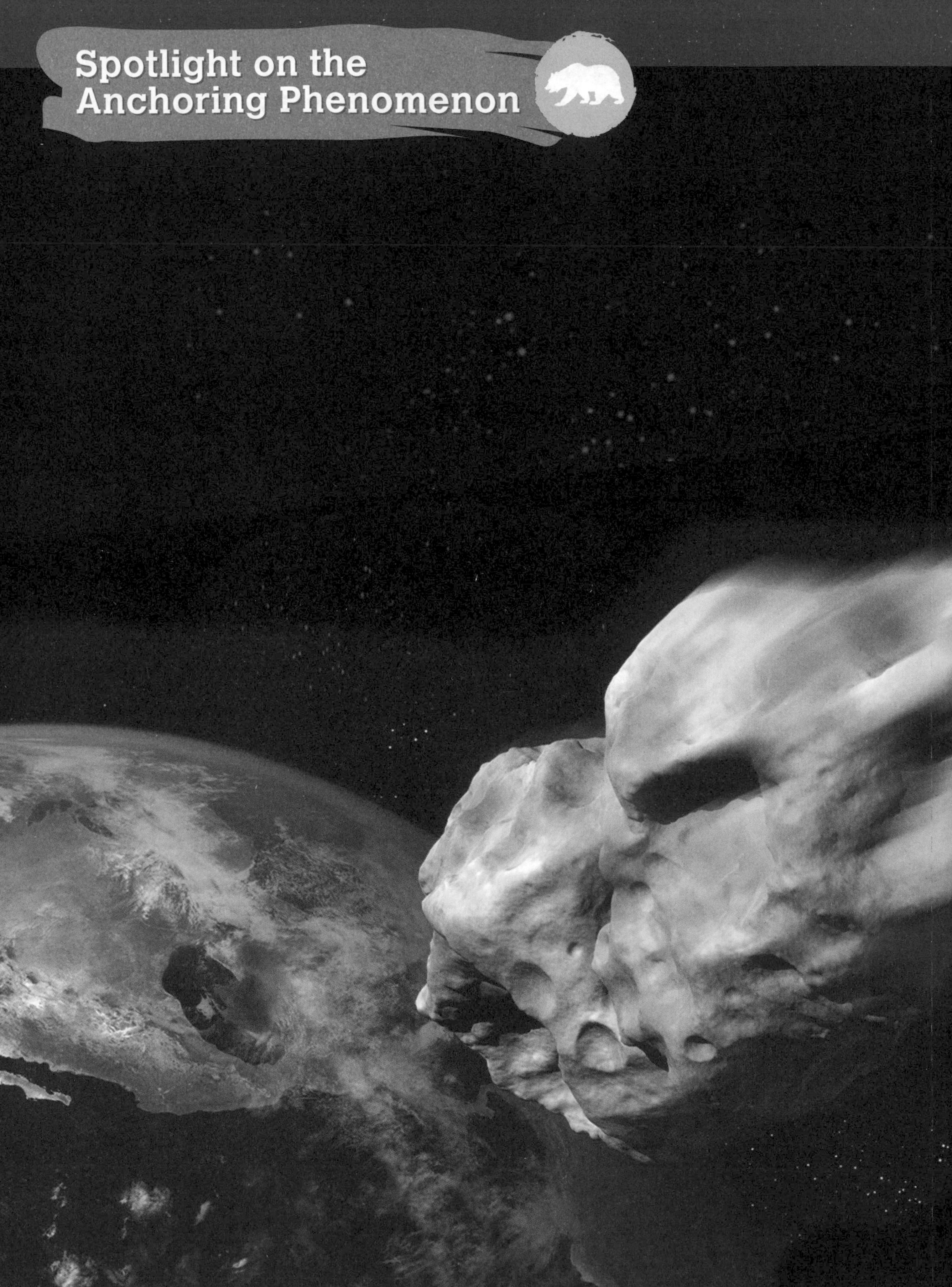
Spotlight on the
Anchoring Phenomenon

How can force and motion be used to predict and minimize the impacts of collisions?

Explore It

Look at the picture. What do you observe? What questions do you have about the phenomenon? Write your observations and questions in the space below.

California Spotlight

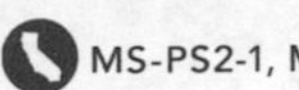

Instructional Segment 1

MS-PS2-1, MS-PS2-2, MS-PS2-4

Inquiry

- What are forces and how do they affect the motions of objects?
- What happens when a moving object collides with something?
- Do objects always need a force in order to keep moving?

Topic

1 Forces and Motion

2 Energy

Before the Topics

Identify the Problem

Hunting Asteroids in California

Phenomenon What would you do if you turned on the TV one afternoon only to learn that a huge asteroid was hurtling through space toward California?

In 2016, officials from the National Aeronautics and Space Administration (NASA) and the Federal Emergency Management Agency (FEMA) gathered in Los Angeles to answer that very question. In a carefully planned simulation, they considered the possibility of an asteroid striking southern California and how they could work together to respond to the disaster.

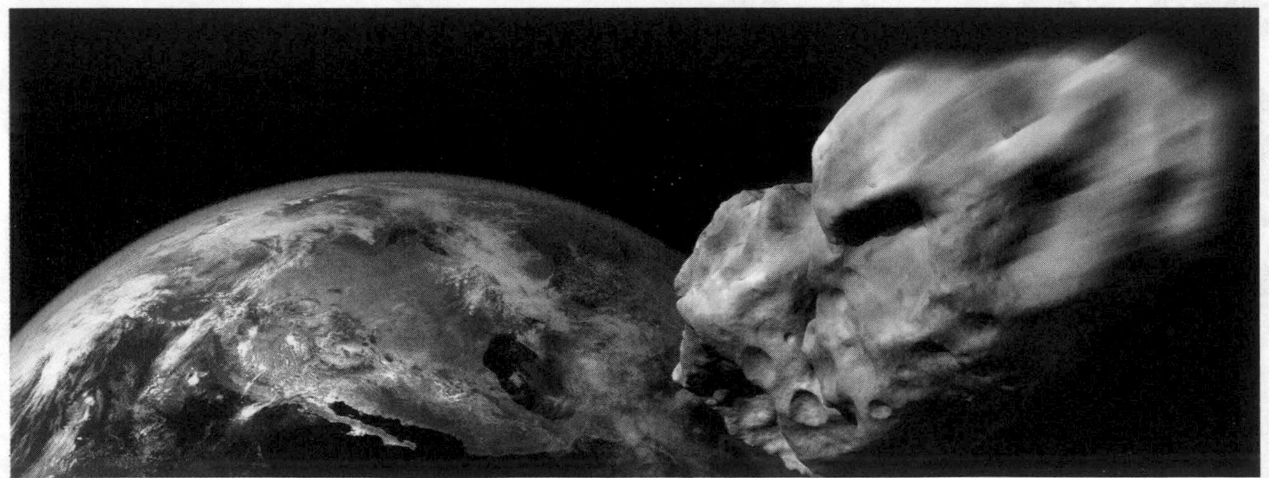

An asteroid striking the west coast of the United States would cause a devastating impact.

Catastrophic Impacts

While objects do commonly encounter our planet, most are relatively small. They either burn up in the atmosphere or cause limited damage when they hit. Still, there is good reason for scientists to be concerned. Some massive asteroids have struck Earth, and some of these collisions have been devastating to life on the planet. Scientists, for example, believe that the asteroid impact that formed the Chicxulub crater about 66 million years ago caused or contributed to the loss of 80 percent of life on Earth, including dinosaurs. The collision instantly changed the stable conditions that had allowed life to flourish on the planet. The energy released by the impact produced a fireball that consumed everything in its path. Vaporized rock was thrown into the atmosphere. Ash rained back down to Earth, igniting fires far beyond the impact zone. Dust and soot filled the atmosphere, filtering out sunlight and causing the planet's average temperature to cool.

The map shows the locations of impact craters discovered on Earth with radii 100 km or larger. Scientists think that there are other large craters waiting to be discovered.

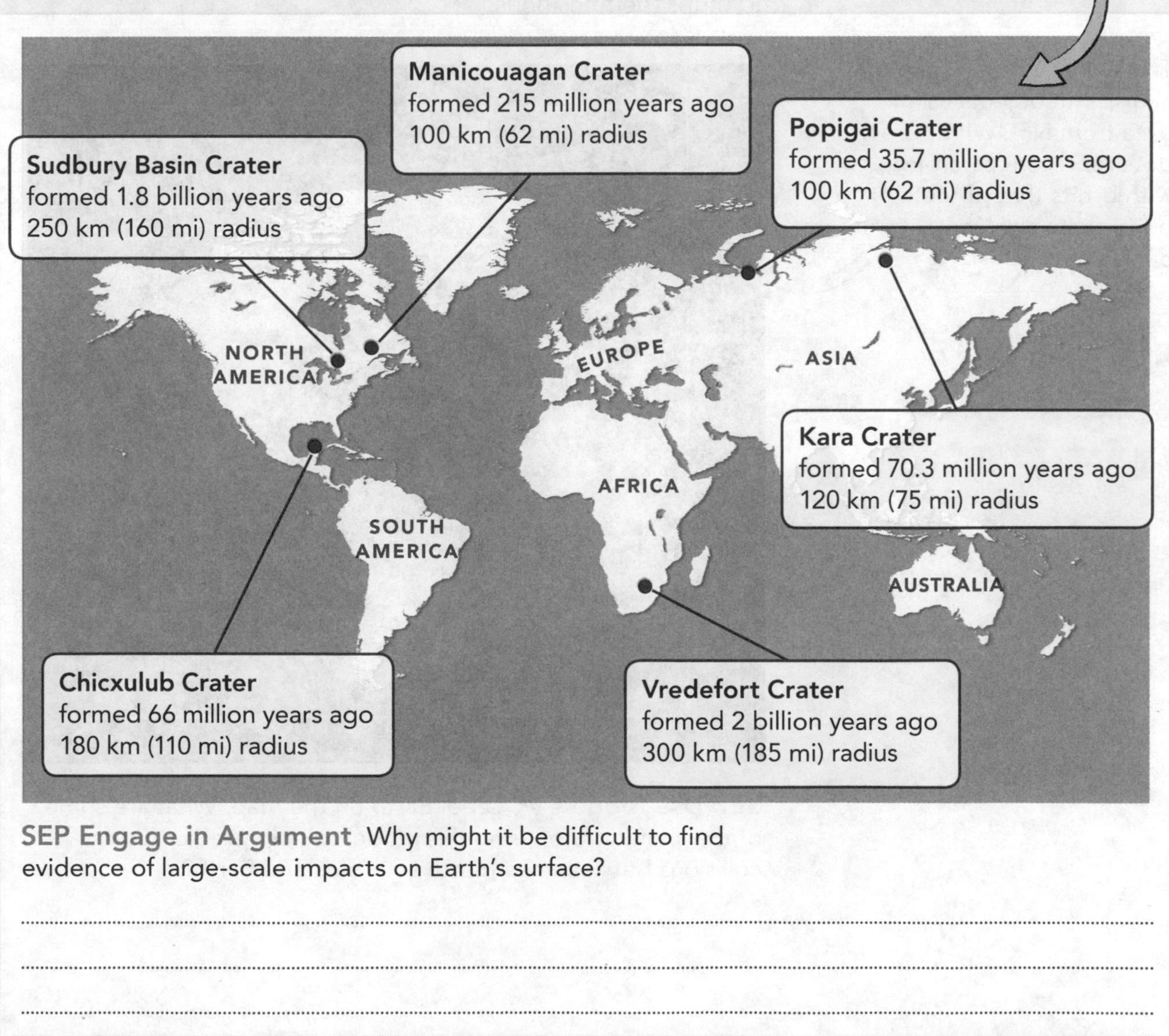

SEP Engage in Argument Why might it be difficult to find evidence of large-scale impacts on Earth's surface?

....

....

....

Watching the Skies

Scientists in California are at the forefront of efforts to avoid another Chicxulub. At the Jet Propulsion Laboratory (JPL) in Pasadena and other facilities in California, scientists are using powerful technology and supercomputers to hunt for asteroids. They also track the positions of known asteroids and develop methods to avoid future impacts, ensuring that we don't suffer the same the fate as the dinosaurs.

JPL maintains the Small-Body Database, which is a growing catalogue with over 16,000 asteroids and other small bodies whose orbits bring them near Earth. JPL researchers estimate that over 1,000 of these near-Earth objects are potentially hazardous.

To get a better picture of these possible threats, the Science Data Center for NASA's Near-Earth Object Wide-field Infrared Survey Explorer (NEOWISE) satellite data about thousands of asteroids and maps their positions.

This is a composite map of near-Earth objects using data from NEOWISE. Green dots represent asteroids with orbits that potentially bring them into contact with our planet.

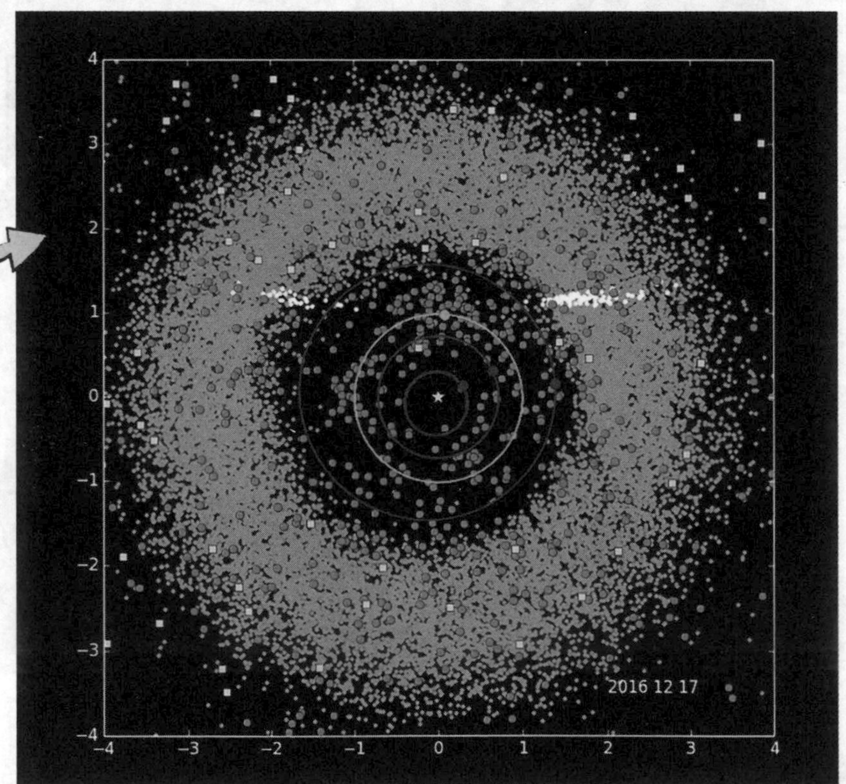

SEP Use Models Label Earth on the map. What are some of the limitations of using this model to help predict future collisions between near-Earth asteroids and Earth?

....

....

....

Calculating Risks

The Center for Near-Earth Object Studies (CNEOS) is part of JPL's impact monitoring system. CNEOS is devoted to calculating the orbits of potentially hazardous objects and determining their chances of striking our planet. Researchers use models and computer simulations to help them predict the paths of these asteroids and other objects. The center is constantly updating data about every known asteroid's path, speed, and impact risk.

CNEOS runs two different monitoring systems. The Sentry system provides long-term projections for possible future impacts. The Scout system calculates and predicts the movements of newly-discovered objects. Sentry, for example, has determined that asteroid 2010 GZ60 will come within striking distance of Earth 480 times between 2017 and 2116.

This computer simulation was created by NASA/JPL based on observations and calculations. It shows that a small asteroid traveling at about 7.8 km/s (17,400 mi/hr) would pass about 27,700 km (17,200 mi) from Earth on February 15, 2013. The geosynchronous satellite ring on the diagram represents the outer distance at which some satellites orbit Earth.

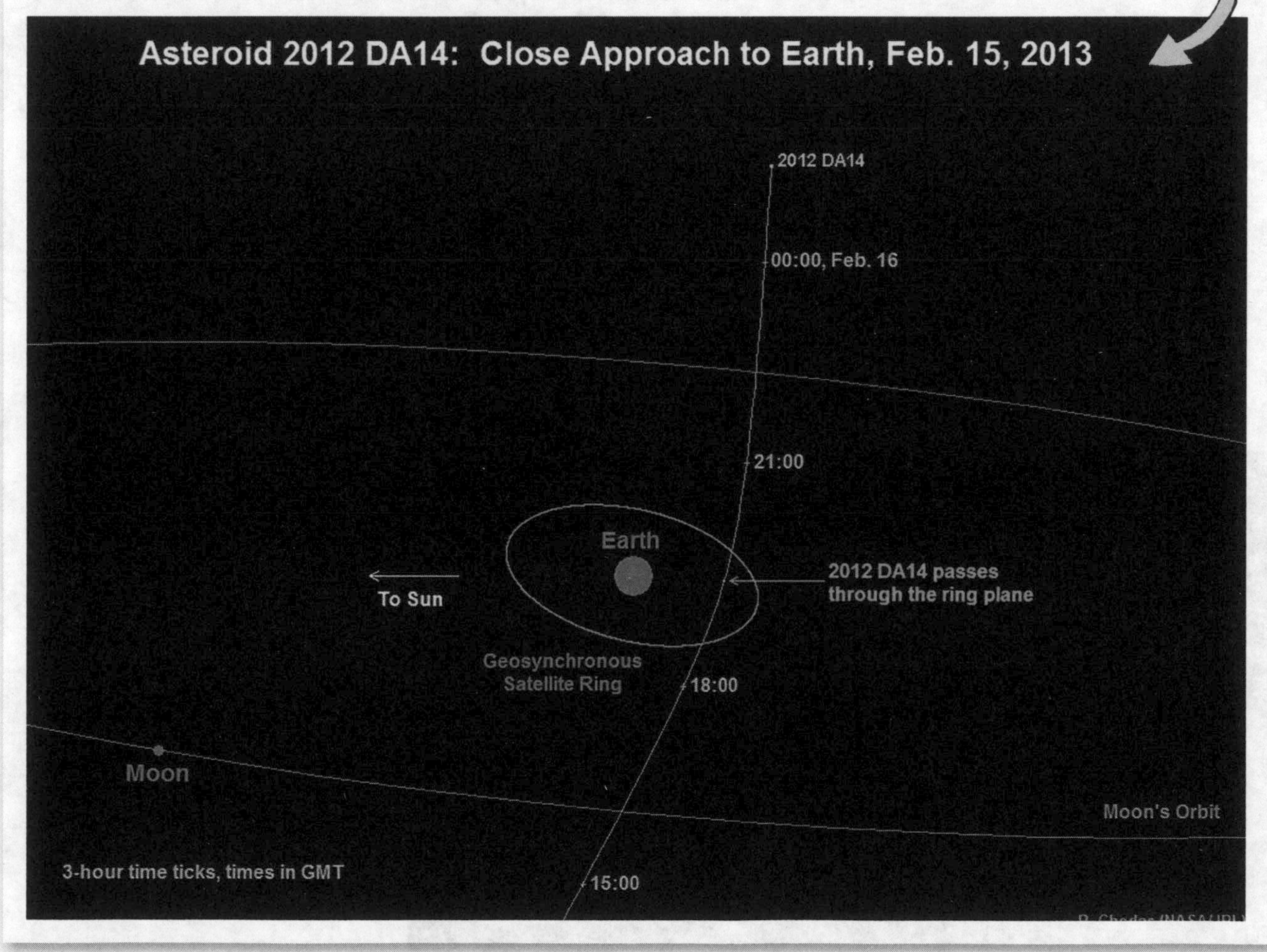

A Close Call?

In 2017, NASA scientists had their eyes on asteroid Florence, which had been first observed in 1981. According to their calculations, this large asteroid was due to pass near Earth in September. Luckily, its path would keep it 7 million km (4.4 million mi) from our planet. But CNEOS's manager put things into perspective before Florence approached: "Florence is the largest asteroid to pass by our planet this close since the NASA program to detect and track near-Earth asteroids began."

On September 1, JPL's Goldstone Deep Space Communications Complex in Fort Irwin took radar images of Florence. The images revealed that the 4.4 km (2.7 mi) asteroid has two moons orbiting it.

JPL engineers are hard at work exploring how potentially hazardous asteroids might be deflected away from Earth. To predict the paths of asteroids and develop methods to avoid impacts, scientists must understand the forces that act between Earth and near-Earth objects and how these forces affect their motions and energy. In these topics, you will learn about the relationships among energy, force, and motion so that you can develop an asteroid deflection plan to submit to NASA.

In addition to capturing the asteroid's two moons, imaging by the Goldstone Deep Space radar in Fort Irwin, California, revealed Florence to be nearly round.

Inner Moon
Outer Moon
3122 Florence

Ask Questions

What questions can you ask to help you make sense of this phenomena?

TOPIC

1

Forces and Motion

Investigative Phenomenon

How can you use models to demonstrate how the motion of an object will be affected by forces that act on it?

MS-PS2-1 Apply Newton's Third Law to design a solution to a problem involving the motion of two colliding objects.

MS-PS2-2 Plan an investigation to provide evidence that the change in an object's motion depends on the sum of the forces on the object and the mass of the object.

MS-PS2-4 Construct and present arguments using evidence to support the claim that gravitational interactions are attractive and depend on the masses of interacting objects.

MS-PS3-1 Construct and interpret graphical displays of data to describe the relationships of kinetic energy to the mass of an object and to the speed of an object.

MS-PS3-2 Develop a model to describe that when the arrangement of objects interacting at a distance changes, different amounts of potential energy are stored in the system.

EP&CIa Students should be developing an understanding that the goods produced by natural systems are essential to human life and to the functioning of our economies and cultures.

EP&CIIb Students should be developing an understanding that methods used to extract, harvest, transport, and consume natural resources influence the geographic extent, composition, biological diversity, and viability of natural systems.

HANDS-ON LAB

uConnect Determine a reference frame for two different observers.

What forces act on these skydivers?

What questions do you have about the investigative phenomenon?

Quest PBL

How can you take the crash out of a collision?

STEM **Figure It Out** When engineers design amusement park rides, they have to consider all of the forces that will be acting on riders and make sure the rides are safe. Engineers test their designs with dummies to ensure that riders will not fall out of their seats and collisions will not cause injuries. In this problem-based Quest activity, you will apply your knowledge of Newton's laws of motion to design a bumper car ride that is safe—for both the rider and the bumper car. You will explore forces and Newton's third law of motion as you design, build, test, and refine a model bumper car. As you carry out your research, focus on small questions, and use different sources to find answers.

MS-PS2-1

INTERACTIVITY

Build a Better Bumper Car

NBC LEARN VIDEO

After watching the Quest Kickoff video, which examines forces and the laws of motion, think about amusement park rides. Complete the 3-2-1 activity.

3 things riders want to experience

....

....

....

2 ways that rides keep riders safe

....

....

1 way in which riders sometimes get injured

....

....

Quest CHECK-IN

IN LESSON 1

STEM What criteria and constraints must engineers consider when designing a safe ride? Think about the goals of the project and how you will ensure a positive outcome.

INTERACTIVITY

Define Criteria and Constraints

Quest CHECK-IN

IN LESSON 2

How do mass and speed affect collisions? Observe and collect data on how mass and speed affect collisions.

HANDS-ON LAB

Mass, Speed, and Colliding Cars

Quest CHECK-IN

IN LESSON 3

STEM How do varying masses and rates of speed affect bumper cars and their riders? Develop and evaluate a design for a safe and fun bumper car.

INTERACTIVITY

Apply Newton's Laws of Motion

Every time a bumper car moves forward and hits another car, there is an equal push in the opposite direction. That is part of what makes riding bumper cars fun.

Quest CHECK-IN

IN LESSON 4

STEM How do the action-reaction forces affect bumper cars and their riders? Build, test, evaluate, and improve your bumper car model.

HANDS-ON LAB

Bumping Cars, Bumper Solutions

Quest FINDINGS

Complete the Quest!

Present your final design and explain how you applied Newton's third law of motion as you developed your design.

INTERACTIVITY

Reflect on Your Bumper Car Solution

LESSON 1

Describing Motion and Force

HANDS-ON LAB

uInvestigate Explore how to tell whether an object you are observing is in motion.

MS-PS2-2 Plan an investigation to provide evidence that the change in an object's motion depends on the sum of the forces on the object and the mass of the object.

Connect It!

What part of the image indicates that there is motion? Circle or label it with the word "motion."

SEP Constructing Explanations Why did you label that part of the image?

Apply Scientific Reasoning This image shows a car traveling down a road. Why do you think the trees in the background do not appear to be moving?

An Object in Motion

How do you decide whether something is moving? For example, if you were the driver of the car in **Figure 1**, would you say the trees are moving past you? From the perspective of the driver, the trees seem to be moving. But to the person taking the photograph from the roadway, the car and its driver appear to be moving past the trees. What determines whether the car and driver are moving or not?

INTERACTIVITY

Discover how to use reference frames in relative motion.

VIRTUAL LAB

Learn about launching a spacecraft into motion.

Reference Frames An object is in **motion** if its position changes when compared to another object. A **reference frame** is a place or object used for comparison to determine whether something is in motion. Objects that are fixed to Earth—such as a tree, a stop sign, or a building—make good reference frames. Suppose a tree along the road in **Figure 1** is used as a reference frame. Both the car and the driver inside move past the tree. In relation to the tree, the driver changes position and therefore is in motion. However, if you are photographing the driver from inside the car, then the driver's position does not change. You could say that, compared to you, the driver is not in motion. You must state your reference frame. If you do not share what the frame is, your description is incomplete.

CHECK POINT **Determine Conclusions** Suppose that you are in the car with the driver. What might be your frame of reference, other than yourself, if you determine that the driver is not moving?

....

....

Movin' Along

Figure 1 This car is traveling down US 101 in Crescent City, California. The car is moving in relation to the person taking the photograph.

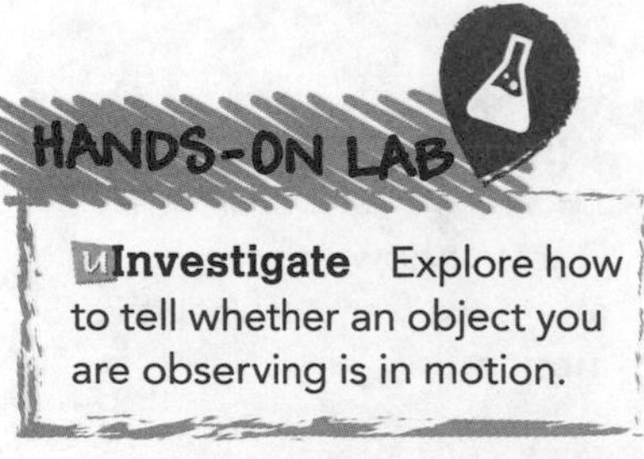

Investigate Explore how to tell whether an object you are observing is in motion.

Academic Vocabulary
In this lesson, *relative* means "not fixed, not absolute." What does *relative* mean when you use it as a noun?

Relative Motion

Relative Motion Because motion is determined by a reference frame that can change, motion is **relative**. Suppose you are relaxing on a beach. If you use your beach towel as your reference frame, you are not moving. You and the beach towel are not changing positions relative to each other. Suppose you use the sun as a reference frame instead of your beach towel. If you compare your position to the sun, you are moving quite rapidly, because you are on Earth and Earth revolves around the sun. Relative to the sun, you are moving, but relative to Earth, you are sitting still, so you don't feel as if you are in motion. See **Figure 2** for another example of relative motion.

CHECK POINT **Draw Evidence** What sources of information might you use to determine the relative motion of Earth compared to other planets in the solar system?

Relative Motion
Figure 2 Motion is relative on this roller coaster in Vallejo, California. Circle the person on the right side of the front car. In the table, list three reference frames that could be used to show that the person is in motion. List three reference frames that could be used to show that the person is stationary.

In motion relative to...	Stationary relative to...

How Forces Affect Motion

While objects move relative to one another, they can also speed up, slow down, and change direction. The motion of an object can change when one or more forces act on the object. A **force** is a push or a pull. When one object pushes or pulls another object, the first object exerts a force on the second object. You exert a force on a book when you push it into your book bag. You exert a force on the sleeve of your jacket when you pull it off your arm.

A bird sits on top of an elephant.

A horse starts pulling a man in a buggy.

A cat pushes a dog.

Describing Force A force is described by its strength and by the direction in which it acts. The force needed to lift a dinner plate requires less strength than the force needed to push a refrigerator. Pushing a faucet handle to the left is a different force from pushing it to the right. In an image, the direction and strength of a force acting on an object can be represented with an arrow. The arrow points in the direction of the force, as shown in **Figure 3**. The length of the arrow indicates the strength of the force—the longer the arrow, the greater the force. In the International System of Units (SI), the unit for the strength of a force is called a **newton** (N), after the scientist Sir Isaac Newton.

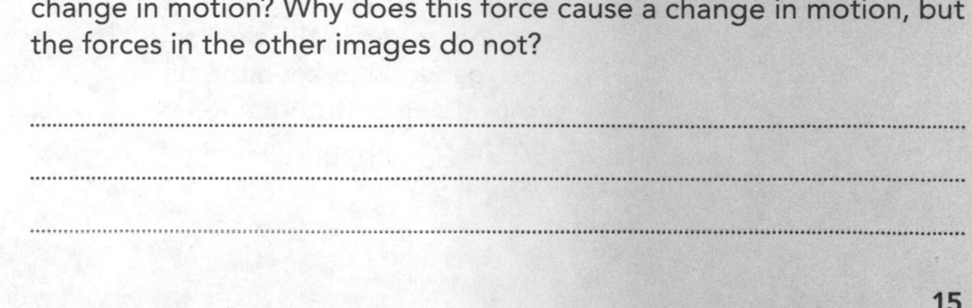

Representing Forces

Figure 3 ✎ In the first image, a short arrow in a downward direction shows that the bird is exerting a small downward force on the elephant. Draw arrows on the other images to represent the size and direction of the forces applied by the animals in action.

CCC Cause and Effect Which image shows a force that causes a change in motion? Why does this force cause a change in motion, but the forces in the other images do not?

....

....

....

VIDEO

Learn about describing motion and force.

Literacy Connection

Draw Evidence Use an additional source to find out what a "normal" force is. Is a normal force a contact force or a noncontact force? What is the normal force on a single book on a shelf?

Types of Forces

Forces can be classified as either contact forces or noncontact forces. Contact forces are those applied only when one object actually touches another. When you push a box across the floor, your push is a contact force because the force only exists while you touch the box. The box may be difficult to push because there is another contact force acting on the box in the opposite direction of your push. It is the force of friction between the box and the floor. **Friction** is a contact force that two surfaces exert on each other when they rub against each other. Friction between your feet and the sidewalk prevents you from slipping as you walk. Ice on the sidewalk greatly reduces that friction.

A noncontact force is a force applied to an object whether it touches the object or not. One noncontact force that you experience every day is **gravity**—a force that pulls objects toward each other as a result of their masses. The force of gravity pulls your body toward Earth. Magnetism and electrical forces are also noncontact forces. **Figure 4** shows examples of contact forces and noncontact forces.

CHECK POINT **Identify** What are three examples of noncontact forces?

Contact and Noncontact Forces

Figure 4 You use contact and noncontact forces daily. Complete the sentence in each caption by underlining either "contact" or "noncontact."

This girl exerts a force on the pedals of this bicycle, and friction between the tires and the road help to keep the bike from slipping. Both the force on the pedals and friction are (contact/noncontact) forces.

Even when your feet don't touch the ground, gravity pulls you toward Earth's surface. Gravity is a (contact/noncontact) force.

Balanced and Unbalanced Forces

More than one force can act on an object. If two forces acting on an object are equal in strength and opposite in direction, they are balanced forces. A single book resting on a shelf has two forces acting on it. The downward force of gravity is equal in strength and opposite in direction to the upward force of the shelf on the book. The forces are balanced, and the system is stable.

What happens when someone pulls the book off the shelf? The pull of the person removing the book and the friction between the shelf and the book also act in opposite directions. These two forces, however are not equal in strength. The pull is stronger than the friction. These forces are unbalanced.

When the forces on an object are unbalanced, there is a nonzero net force acting on the object. The **net force** on an object is the combination of all the forces acting on that object. If the forces act in the same direction, the net force is the sum of the forces. If the forces act in opposite directions, the net force is the difference in the strengths of those forces. If the net force turns out to be zero, the forces are balanced. Otherwise, the forces are unbalanced. A nonzero net force acting on an object causes a change in the object's motion.

INTERACTIVITY

Explore balanced and unbalanced forces in action.

Write About It! In your science notebook, describe two examples of how unbalanced forces help you in your everyday life.

VIDEO

Learn about contact and noncontact forces.

Model It!

Forces in Tug-of-War

Figure 5 A tug-of-war competition demonstrates the effects of balanced and unbalanced forces on motion. The people on the left side of the rope are experiencing a force from the rope pulling them to the right. They are also experiencing friction from the ground pushing them to the left. The winning team is the team that experiences the greater force of friction.

SEP Develop Models Draw more people on the left side of the picture to increase the force of friction experienced by the team on the left side of the rope. Add arrows to the model to represent the force from the rope and the force of friction on the people.

Math Toolbox

Effects of Net Force

In each diagram, two animals push on an apple. The forces of gravity and friction acting on the apple in each scenario does not change, so the forces that may cause a change will come from the animals.

Two chipmunks push on the apple in opposite directions with forces of equal strength. The forces on the apple are balanced. The motion and position of the apple do not change.

You can think of the forces in terms of positive and negative numbers. If the force to the right is +2, the force to the left is –2, and the net force, again, is 0.

A chipmunk and a squirrel push on the apple in opposite directions with forces of different strengths. The forces on the apple are unbalanced. In this case, the strength of the net force on the apple is found by subtracting the strength of the smaller force from the strength of the larger force. The net force is in the same direction as the larger force.

A chipmunk and a squirrel push on the apple in the same direction. The forces on the apple are unbalanced. The net force on the apple is the sum of these forces. The apple will start moving to the right.

1. **Write an Inequality** For each set of forces, write one of these signs to compare the forces: =, >, <.

   2 N .... 2 N

   2 N .... 6 N

   8 N .... 0 N

2. **SEP Use Mathematics** Label each diagram with the strength of the net force in newtons (N).

3. **Reason Quantitatively** In the center diagram, which direction will the apple start moving?

   ....

INTERACTIVITY

Check your understanding of net force in this interactivity.

CHECK POINT Infer A girl picks up a bag of apples that are at rest on the floor. How does the force the girl applies compare to the force of gravity acting on the apples?

....

....

....

LESSON 1 Check

MS-PS2-2

1. **Determine Differences** What is the difference between a contact force and a noncontact force?

2. **Apply Scientific Reasoning** A child is riding in a wagon. What reference frame might have been used if an observer said the child was not moving?

3. **SEP Use Mathematics** Two children fight over a toy. One pulls with a force of 8 N to the right. The other pulls with a force of 6 N to the left. What is the strength and direction of the net force on the toy?

4. **SEP Construct Explanations** A cow is grazing in a field. Under what conditions does the cow have relative motion?

5. **CCC Stability and Change** One man pushes on the front of a cart while another man pushes on the back of the cart. The cart begins to move forward. What are three things you know about these two applied forces?

Quest CHECK-IN

In this lesson, you learned about the motion of objects. You also learned about different types of forces and how these forces affect the movement of objects.

Identify What are the forces that act upon amusement park rides? Why is it important for engineers to understand how motion and forces affect the rides they design?

INTERACTIVITY

Define Criteria and Constraints

Go online to identify the problem, consider criteria and constraints, and develop a design for your prototype. Remember that a one of the constraints on a design is usually a budget.

LESSON

2 Speed, Velocity, and Acceleration

HANDS-ON LAB

Investigate Experiment to find out how you can calculate your speed as you walk to your locker.

MS-PS2-2 Plan an investigation to provide evidence that the change in an object's motion depends on the sum of the forces on the object and the mass of the object.

Connect It!

Draw an arrow to show the strength and direction of the force applied to the ground as the skier attempts to turn on his skis.

SEP Construct Explanations How does the snow help the skier move down the hill?

....

....

....

CCC Stability and Change How would you describe the difference in the motion of the skier from when he starts at the top of the slope to when he is halfway down the hill?

....

....

Calculating Speed

You might describe the motion of the skier in **Figure 1** as slow when he starts moving and fast when he reaches the bottom of the slalom course. By using these words, you are describing the skier's speed. The **speed** of an object is the distance the object moves per unit of time. Speed is a type of rate. A rate tells you the amount of something that occurs or changes in one unit of time.

Distance Over Time To calculate the speed of an object, divide the distance the object travels by the amount of time it takes to travel that distance. This relationship can be written as an equation:

$$\text{Speed} = \frac{\text{Distance}}{\text{Time}}$$

Any unit that expresses distance over time is a unit of speed. Some examples of units of speed include kilometers per hour, miles per hour, and feet per minute. When you state a speed, you must include the units. If you do not state the units, the statement is incomplete. The SI unit for speed is meters per second, or m/s. For example, the skier might travel at a speed of 5 m/s near the starting point. This means that the skier travels a distance of 5 meters in 1 second. As the skier nears the bottom of the hill, he might be moving at a speed of about 15 m/s. This means that the skier travels a distance of 15 meters in 1 second. The greater the number of meters per second, the faster the speed at which the object is traveling.

Picking up Speed
Figure 1 This skier is competing at a slalom race in Mammoth Lakes, California. As the skier travels down the course, he moves faster and faster.

Investigate Experiment to find out how you can calculate your speed as you walk to your locker.

Academic Vocabulary

Student Discourse In math, you find an average by dividing the sum of values by the number of values given. Discuss with another class member how you might use the word *average* in a situation that does not involve math.

Instantaneous and Average Speeds

Instantaneous and Average Speeds Think about the last time you rode in a car. Depending on road conditions and traffic, the speed of the vehicle varied. If you had looked at the speedometer for a moment in a traffic jam, it might have read 5 kilometers per hour. On the highway, at a particular instant, it might have read 88 kilometers per hour. The speed at a particular instant in time is called *instantaneous speed.*

Although you did not travel at the same speed for the whole trip, you did have an **average** speed throughout the trip. To calculate average speed, divide the total distance traveled by the total time. For example, suppose you drove a distance of 3 kilometers in 1 hour while in heavy traffic. Then, it took you 1 hour to drive 50 kilometers from one side of a city to the other. Finally, you traveled 211 kilometers on an interstate highway in 2 hours. The average speed of the car is the total distance traveled divided by the total time. In the equation below, you can see that your average speed on the road trip was 66 kilometers per hour.

$$\text{Total distance} = 3\text{ km} + 50\text{ km} + 211\text{ km} = 264\text{ km}$$

$$\text{Total time} = 1\text{ h} + 1\text{ h} + 2\text{ h} = 4\text{ h}$$

$$\text{Average speed} = \frac{264\text{ km}}{4\text{ h}} = 66\text{ km/h}$$

CHECK POINT **Explain** How does instantaneous speed differ from average speed?

Average Speed

Figure 2 A racecar at the the Sonoma County Raceway in California zips around the track. It travels the first 80 kilometers in 0.4 hour. The next 114 kilometers take 0.6 hour. The following 80 kilometers take 0.4 hour. SEP Use Mathematics Calculate the racecar's average speed.

Calculating Speed From a Graph

The graph you see on this page is a distance-versus-time graph. Time is shown on the horizontal axis, or x-axis. Distance is shown on the vertical axis, or y-axis. A point on the line represents the distance an object has traveled during a given time period. The x value of the point is time, and the y value is distance. The angle of a line on a graph is called **slope**. The slope tells you how one **variable** changes in relation to the other variable in the graph. In other words, slope tells you the rate of change. You can calculate the slope of a line by dividing the rise by the run. The rise is the vertical difference between any two points on the line. The run is the horizontal difference between the same two points.

$$\text{Slope} = \frac{\text{Rise}}{\text{Run}}$$

The points in the graph below show a rise of 50 meters and a run of 2 seconds. To find the slope, divide 50 meters by 2 seconds. The slope is 25 meters per second. What do you notice about the units of slope? On a distance-versus-time graph, the units of the slope of the line are the same as the units for speed. Because speed is the rate that distance changes in relation to time, the slope of a distance-versus-time graph represents speed. The steeper the slope is, the greater the speed. A constant slope represents motion at constant speed.

Explore the speed of a space probe using a distance-versus-time motion graph.

Academic Vocabulary

A variable is a letter or symbol that represents a number that can change. Use *variable* as an adjective in a sentence. Explain what it means.

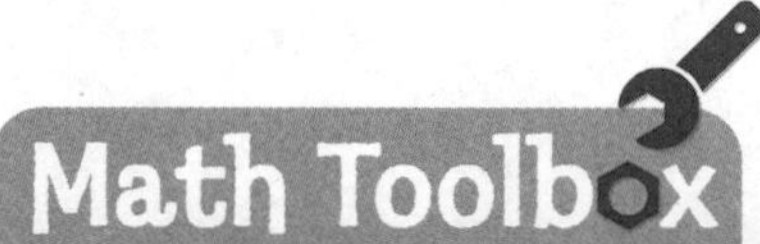

Using a Distance-Versus-Time Graph

The cheetah in this photograph is running at a constant speed. The graph shows the distance the cheetah moves and the time it takes the cheetah to move that distance.

Cheetah's Motion

Distance (m): 0, 20, 40, 60, 80, 100
Time (s): 0, 1, 2, 3, 4
A (0,0)
B (2,50)

1. Calculate Mark two new points on the line. Use these points to calculate the slope.

2. Draw Conclusions What is the average speed of the cheetah?

3. Solve Linear Equations The graph of a straight line that goes through the origin can be represented with the equation $y = mx$. This equation describes the relationship between the two variables x and y. In this equation, m represents the constant slope of the line. Use this equation to determine the distance the cheetah traveled in 4 seconds.

Velocity in Formations

Figure 3 Each member in this marching band must move at a specific velocity to be in the correct place in the formation.

SEP Apply Scientific Reasoning Do all of the members of the band have to move at the same velocity at all times? Explain your reasoning.

....

....

....

....

....

....

....

....

Describing Velocity

To describe an object's motion, you also need to know its direction. For example, suppose you hear that a thunderstorm is traveling at a speed of 25 km/h. Should you prepare for the storm? That depends on the direction in which the storm is moving. If it is traveling toward you, you might want to take cover. The speed at which an object travels in a given direction is called **velocity**. You know the velocity of a storm when you know that it is moving 25 km/h eastward.

In certain situations, describing the velocity of moving objects is important. For example, air traffic controllers must keep close track of the velocities of aircraft. These velocities change as airplanes move overhead and on the runways. An error in determining a velocity, either in speed or in direction, could lead to a collision.

INTERACTIVITY

Investigate the speed, velocity, and acceleration of a skydiver falling for velocity.

CHECK POINT **Determine Conclusions** How can understanding velocity help to prevent a midair collision?

....

....

....

....

Determining Acceleration

Speed and velocity are not the only ways to describe motion. Suppose you are a passenger in a car stopped at a red light. When the light changes to green, the driver steps on the gas pedal. As a result, the car speeds up, or accelerates. But acceleration means more than just speeding up. Scientists define **acceleration** as the rate at which velocity changes. A change in velocity can involve a change in speed, in direction, or both. In science, when an object accelerates, it increases speed, decreases speed, or changes direction.

Change in Speed or Direction When the term *acceleration* is used, it means one of two things—any change in speed or any change in direction. A dog that starts running to chase a squirrel is accelerating. You accelerate when you start walking faster to get to class on time. When objects slow down, they are also accelerating. A car accelerates as it comes to a stop at a red light. A water skier accelerates as the boat slows down. A decrease in speed is sometimes called *deceleration*.

Even an object that is traveling at a constant speed is accelerating when it changes direction. Therefore, a car accelerates as it follows a gentle curve in the road or changes lanes. Runners accelerate as they round the curve in a track.

Model It!

Acceleration

Figure 4 This image shows a basketball player shooting a ball.

1. SEP Develop Models Label the two sections of the path to identify where the ball's speed increases and decreases.

2. SEP Use Models Besides the labels for changing speed, what is another way that you can tell from this model that the ball is accelerating?

....

....

....

Collisions

Remember that any object in motion has energy of motion. The bumper cars shown on this page have speed, and so they have energy of motion.

What happens when a bumper car that is moving hits a bumper car that is not moving? The moving car causes the unmoving car to start moving. There are two ways to look at this. One way to look at it is by using forces. In the collision, the moving car applies a push to the unmoving car, and that force causes the second car to start moving. In other words, the first car causes the second car to accelerate.

Another way to look at it is with energy of motion. The first car has energy of motion, while the second car has none. When they collide, the first car transfers some of its energy of motion to the second car. The first car loses some energy of motion. The second car gains energy of motion and starts to move.

LESSON 2 Check

MS-PS2-2

1. **CCC Stability and Change** What three changes in motion show that an object is accelerating?

2. **Calculate** What is the average speed of a train that covers 80 km in 1 h, 200 km in 2 h, and 420 km in 4 h?

3. **SEP Engage in Argument** A ball is pushed from a stop and rolls 6 m in 2 s. Student A says the average speed of the ball is 3 m/s. Student B says the average speed of the ball is 1.5 m/s^2. Which student is correct? Explain your answer.

4. **SEP Interpret Data** A student graphed distance versus time for an object that moves 14 m every 2 s. What is the speed of the object?

Quest CHECK-IN

In this lesson, you learned how motion can be described in terms of speed, velocity, and acceleration. You also learned how to use mathematical formulas to calculate and graph average speed.

SEP Use Models How might you use a model of a bumper car to determine how speed and acceleration affect the motion of the car? What materials might you use? How would a budget affect your model?

HANDS-ON LAB

Mass, Speed, and Colliding Cars

Go online to download the lab worksheet. Learn about the features of bumper cars that affect acceleration, including positive acceleration, deceleration, and changes in direction. Brainstorm additional features that might affect speed in bumper cars.

LESSON

3 Newton's Laws of Motion

MS-PS2-1 Apply Newton's Third Law to design a solution to a problem involving the motion of two colliding objects.

MS-PS2-2 Plan an investigation to provide evidence that the change in an object's motion depends on the sum of the forces on the object and the mass of the object.

Connect It!

The tennis player is about to hit the tennis ball. Draw an arrow on the image to indicate the direction of the tennis ball.

CCC Cause and Effect How will the motion of the ball change as a result of being hit?

....

....

CCC Stability and Change After being hit, the ball traveled through the air at a constant speed. What might cause its motion to change?

....

....

Newton's First Law of Motion

Explore what causes a ball to stop rolling by taking a poll.

Suppose you are watching a tennis match. You would be surprised if a tennis ball that was sitting still on the court suddenly started moving without being hit. You would also be surprised if a moving ball suddenly stopped in the middle of the air. Your surprise would be the result of knowing that a net force must act upon an object to cause a change in motion. This natural phenomenon is empirical evidence that supports Newton's first law of motion.

Newton's first law of motion states that an object at rest will remain at rest unless acted upon by a nonzero net force. Therefore, a tennis ball that is sitting still will remain at rest unless a player hits it, applying a net force. This law also states that an object moving at a constant velocity will continue moving at a constant velocity unless acted upon by a nonzero net force. You can see this law in action when a tennis ball travels across the court after being hit. The motion remains constant until it hits another player's racket.

A simple statement of Newton's first law of motion is that if an object is not moving, it will not start moving until a net force acts on it. If an object is moving, it will continue at a constant velocity until a net force acts to change its speed or its direction. If there is a net force acting on an object, it will accelerate.

Literacy Connection

Use Information As you read these pages, underline information you can use to define Newton's first law.

Speeding Up

Figure 1 This tennis player is competing at the Olympic Sports Festival in Los Angeles, California. When her racket meets the tennis ball, the ball will change direction.

Mass and Inertia

Figure 2 Suppose each of these women wants to move the dog off of her lap.

Apply Concepts Which dog has less inertia? Which dog is harder to move?

....

Inertia Resistance to change in motion is called **inertia**. So Newton's first law is also called the law of inertia. Inertia explains many common events, including why seat belts and air bags are used in vehicles. If you are riding in a moving car, you are moving at the same speed the car is moving. When brakes apply a force to the car, the car decelerates. The brakes do not apply a force to you, however, so inertia keeps you moving forward at the same speed you and direction were going before the car decelerated. A force, such as the pull of a seat belt, is needed to pull you back.

Inertia and Mass Which object—you or the car—is harder to stop? Based on your own experience, you can probably figure out that the car is harder to stop. That is because it has more mass. The more massive object has a greater inertia, as in **Figure 2**.

Once Newton had described the connection between inertia and mass, he next figured out how to find the acceleration of an object when a force acted on it.

CHECK POINT **Summarize** How does mass relate to inertia?

....

....

Newton's Second Law of Motion

Newton's first law stated that inertia exists for an object. Newton then explained that an object's mass directly affects how much force is needed to accelerate the object.

Changes in Acceleration and Mass Suppose that you apply a constant net force to an object. How does changing the mass of the object affect its acceleration? You can see the effect with a horse-drawn sleigh, shown in **Figure 3**. The horses provide a steady force. If the sleigh is empty, it will accelerate quickly when the horses pull on it. If the sleigh is full of people, it has a greater inertia and will accelerate slowly. The acceleration of the sleigh will change depending on the mass of the load it carries. Suppose you want the loaded sleigh to have same acceleration as the empty sleigh. Then the horses would have to pull the greater mass of the loaded sleigh with a greater force. Newton understood these relationships and found a way to represent them mathematically.

Calculating Force Newton's second law of motion states that the size and direction of a net force equals the mass times the acceleration. The net force will have the same direction as the acceleration. This relationship can be written as follows:

$$\text{Net force} = \text{Mass} \times \textbf{Acceleration} \text{ or } F = m \times a$$

If the net force and mass are known, the resulting acceleration can be **derived** by using this equation:

$$\text{Acceleration} = \frac{\text{Net force}}{\text{Mass}} \text{ or } a = \frac{F}{m}$$

Academic Vocabulary

Student Discourse Read the sentence in which the word *derived* is used, and discuss with the class what the word means.

Newton's Second Law

Figure 3 At the Rose Parade in Pasadena, California, the force applied by the horses pulls the carriage and the people it contains.

1. **CCC Cause and Effect** How might you change the number of people to increase the carriage's acceleration?

2. **CCC Cause and Effect** How might you change the number of people to decrease the carriage's acceleration?

INTERACTIVITY

Explore how mass, motion, and force are related.

Calculations with Newton's Second Law

As you have already seen, the formula for Newton's second law can be written to solve for force or acceleration. Newton's second law can also be written to solve for mass.

You already know that acceleration is measured in meters per second squared (m/s^2), and that mass is measured in kilograms (kg). When you multiply mass and acceleration according to Newton's second law, you find that force is measured in kilograms times meters per second squared ($kg\text{-}m/s^2$). This unit is also called a newton (N), which is the SI unit of force. One newton is the force required to give a 1-kg mass an acceleration of 1 m/s^2.

CHECK POINT **Apply Concepts** Based on what you've learned, derive another equation for Newton's second law that is written to solve for mass. Use the variables *a*, *F*, and *m*.

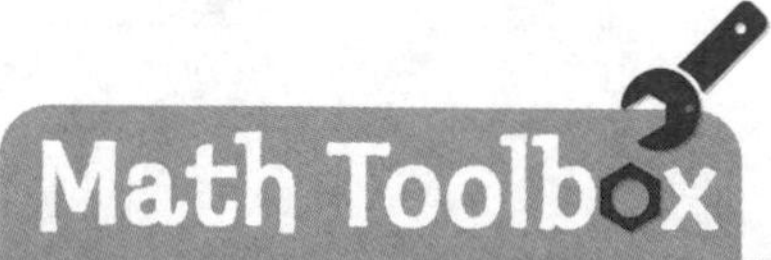

Math Toolbox

Using Newton's Second Law

Use the equations for Newton's second law to understand how mass and force affect the motion of a volleyball.

Evaluate Expressions Show your calculations for each problem.

a. A volleyball is hit and experiences a net force of 2 N, which causes it to accelerate at 8 m/s^2. What is the mass of the volleyball?

b. The same ball is hit again and experiences a net force of 3.5 N, a greater force. Is the change in motion greater or less?

c. The same ball rolls horizontally along the sand and decelerates at a rate of 6 m/s^2. Calculate the force of friction that caused this deceleration.

Newton's Third Law of Motion

A library is full of shelves of books. Gravity pulls each book down. If the shelf did not push upward on each book with equal force, the books would fall. The force exerted by the shelf is equal in strength and opposite in direction to the force the books exert on the shelf. Newton's third law of motion states that if one object exerts a force on another object, then the second object exerts a force of equal strength in the opposite direction on the first object. Another way to state Newton's third law is that for every action there is an equal (in strength) but opposite (in direction) reaction.

Action-Reaction Pairs

Figure 4 When you ride a skateboard, you move along because the ground provides a reaction force to the action force of your foot.

SEP Develop Models ✎ Draw arrows to show the action and reaction forces between the dog and his leash and the gymnast on the beam. Then, draw your own example of action-reaction forces in the space provided.

Action-Reaction Pairs An action force is always paired with a reaction force. Pairs of action and reaction forces are all around you. When you walk, you push backward on the ground with your feet. Think of this as an action force. The ground pushes forward on your feet with an equal and opposite force. This is the reaction force. You can walk only because the ground pushes you forward!

INTERACTIVITY

Use Newton's laws to discover how a baseball player can hit more home runs—going, going, gone!

VIDEO

Learn about Newton's Laws of Motion.

VIDEO

Discover how a mechanical engineer uses science to solve engineering problems.

CHECK POINT
Use Information A dog walks along the ground. If the dog applies an action force on the ground, what is the reaction force?

....

....

....

Detecting Forces and Motion Some results of action-reaction forces are easily observed. If you were a skateboarder, you could feel the force of the ground on your foot. It would be empirical evidence demonstrating the reaction force. If you drop your pen, gravity pulls the pen downward and you can see it fall.

But some changes caused by action-reaction forces are not as easily detected. When you drop your pen, the pen pulls Earth upward with an equal and opposite reaction force, according to Newton's third law. You see the pen fall, but you don't see Earth accelerate toward the pen. Remember Newton's second law. If mass increases and force stays the same, acceleration decreases. The same size force acts on both Earth and your pen. Because Earth has such a large mass, its acceleration is so small that you don't notice it.

Balanced and Action-Reaction Forces You have learned that two equal forces acting in opposite directions on an object balance each other and produce no change in motion. So why aren't the action-reaction forces in Newton's third law of motion balanced as well? In order for forces to balance, they must act on the same object. Action-reaction forces are not balanced because they act on different objects. When a hockey player hits a puck with his stick, the action force is the force of the stick on the puck. The reaction force is the force of the puck on the stick. So one force acts on the puck, while the other acts on the stick. The puck has a much smaller mass than the player and his stick, so you see the puck accelerate. See how other action-reaction forces act on different objects in **Figure 5**.

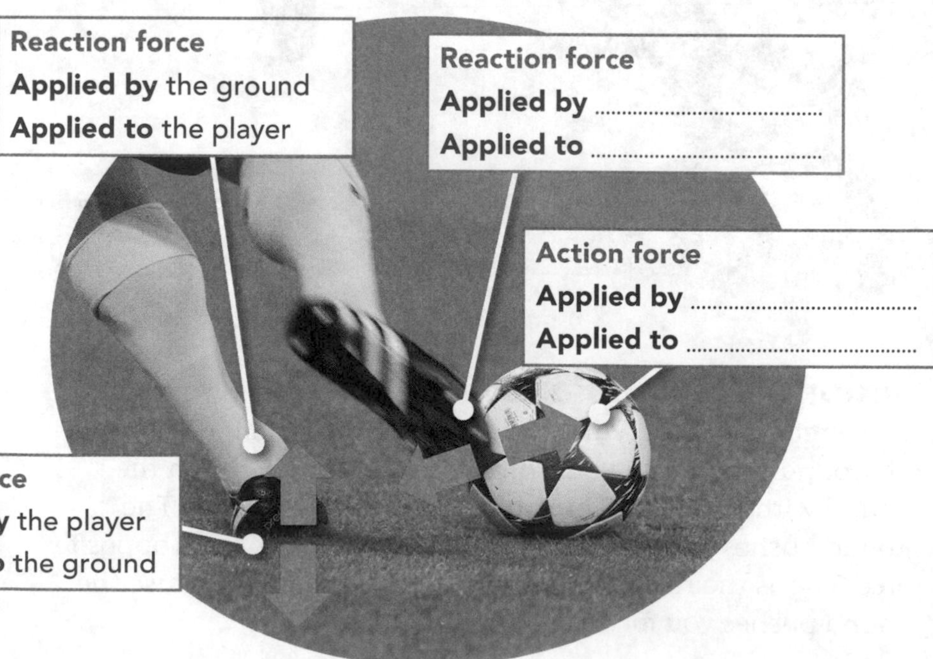

Understanding Action-Reaction

Figure 5 Action-reaction forces are applied to different objects. The action and reaction forces acting on a soccer player, a soccer ball, and the ground are shown with arrows. Finish labeling the forces to describe how they are being applied.

Question It

Applying Newton's Laws

Kirsten has a parakeet that likes to sit on a swing. Sometimes the bird makes the swing move back and forth.

SEP Ask Questions You want to investigate the bird and his swing and how they relate to Newton's laws of motion. List at least two questions you might ask.

....

....

Newton's Laws Together When you have a situation involving force, acceleration, and mass, it usually involves two or even all three of Newton's laws! Look at **Figure 6** to see how Newton's laws apply to an amusement park ride.

Reflect Describe how Newton's laws of motion are involved in an activity in your daily life.

Newton's First Law:	Newton's Second Law:	Newton's Third Law:

Newton's Laws
Figure 6 In each space provided, give an example of a way that one of Newton's laws is shown in this amusement park ride at the Santa Cruz boardwalk in California.

LESSON 3 Check

MS-PS2-1, MS-PS2-2

1. **SEP Communicate Information** In your own words, what is Newton's second law of motion?

2. **Apply Concepts** What is inertia? Use an example in your description.

3. **Integrate Information** What is the difference between balanced forces and action-reaction forces?

4. **CCC Cause and Effect** You push on a door and it opens. Explain what happens in terms of action-reaction forces.

Quest CHECK-IN

In this lesson, you learned how Newton's laws explain the motions of moving objects and how mass affects acceleration. You also learned that every action has an equal and opposite reaction.

Apply Concepts How would Newton's laws of motion relate to the movement of bumper cars? How might the mass of the riders and the speed of the cars affect this movement?

INTERACTIVITY

Apply Newton's Laws of Motion

Go online to learn about how action-reaction forces affect the movement of vehicles in collisions. Then brainstorm how these forces would affect bumper cars. As you carry out your research, make sure to consult a variety of sources. Focus on small questions rather than broad topics.

littleBits™

MS-PS2-1, EP&CIa, EP&CIIb

GENERATING ENERGY from Potholes

INTERACTIVITY

Explore how Newton's laws can be used to design more fuel-efficient vehicles.

Traveling in a car on an uneven road can make for a bouncy ride. How can you capture energy generated by the bouncing? You engineer it!

The Challenge: To convert the motion of a car into electrical energy.

Phenomenon With over 35 million registered vehicles and over 640,000 km (400,000 mi) of roadway in the state, Californians do a lot of driving. What if all these cars and trucks could do more than just use energy and actually generate it? As a car or truck travels down a road, the vehicle exerts an action force on the road and the road exerts and reaction force on the wheels of the vehicle. A bumpy road occasionally exerts a stronger force than a smooth road, which can result in an uncomfortable ride. That's where shock absorbers come in. Shock absorbers are part of a car's suspension system. They steady the ride of a car by slowing the motion of the suspension after the wheels hit a bump.

With traditional shock absorbers, forces exerted by the road transfer energy that is converted to heat. Auto engineers have developed electromechanical shock absorbers that alter the flow of energy. They use a lever arm to capture the up-and-down motion of the wheels. A device called an alternator transforms that kinetic energy input into electricity output. The engineers hope that this electrical energy can be used to increase the fuel efficiency of cars. That will help to reduce the consumption of oil, as well as curbing air pollution and the impact of climate change.

With electromechanical shock absorbers, the energy lost as a car moves over bumps and potholes can be transformed into electrical energy.

Can you build a model to represent a shock absorber? Go to the Engineering Design Notebook to find out!

LESSON 4 Friction and Gravitational Interactions

HANDS-ON LAB

uInvestigate Explore how friction is affected by different surfaces, and investigate how the force of friction affects the motion of objects.

MS-PS2-4 Construct and present arguments using evidence to support the claim that gravitational interactions are attractive and depend on the masses of interacting objects.

MS-PS3-1 Construct and interpret graphical displays of data to describe the relationships of kinetic energy to the mass of an object and to the speed of an object.

MS-PS3-2 Develop a model to describe that when the arrangement of objects interacting at a distance changes, different amounts of potential energy are stored in the system.

Connect It!

Circle two areas that show what causes the bike to slow down.

Identify What force is responsible for stopping the bike?

....

SEP Construct Explanations Is this force a contact or noncontact force? Explain.

....

....

....

Factors That Affect Friction

INTERACTIVITY

Describe your experiences riding a bicycle on different surfaces.

Recall that the force two surfaces exert on each other when they rub against each other is the contact force called *friction*. For example, if you slide a book across a table, the surface of the book rubs against the surface of the table. The resulting force is friction. This force acts in a direction opposite to the motion of the book and eventually stops the book.

Two Factors Both the types of surfaces involved and how hard the surfaces are pushed together affect the friction between two surfaces. The bicyclist in **Figure 1** is using friction to slow his bicycle. One place where friction occurs on the bicycle is between the tires and the ground. Have you ever examined the surface of a tire? The tread on the tire results in more friction between the tire and the ground. A tire on a mountain bike has more tread on it than a regular bike tire, so more of friction is produced between a mountain bike tire and the ground. In general, smoother surfaces produce less friction than rougher surfaces.

In this instance, friction also occurs between the brake pads and the wheels. This friction prevents the tire from turning. The harder the bicyclist applies the brakes, the more quickly the bike will come to a stop. Friction increases as surfaces push harder against each other.

Friction acts in a direction opposite to the direction of the object's motion. Without friction or some other force acting in the opposite direction, a moving object will not stop until it strikes another object.

Skidding to a Stop

Figure 1 California boasts over 800 mountain biking trails across the state. To slow down his bike, this biker applies his brakes and skids.

Types of Friction California is renowned for its skaters and skate parks, such as the Lake Cunningham Regional Skate Park in San Jose, the largest in the state. A skate park is a great place to see friction at work. Use **Figure 2** to find out more about four different types of friction.

CHECK POINT **Write Arguments** How can you be sure that the skater leaping through the air feels less force than the one speeding along the ground?

....

....

Friction in a Skate Park

Figure 2 Add labels to three other skaters in the figure to identify the type of friction that is opposing their motion. Then, for each type of friction described, identify another example of that type of friction.

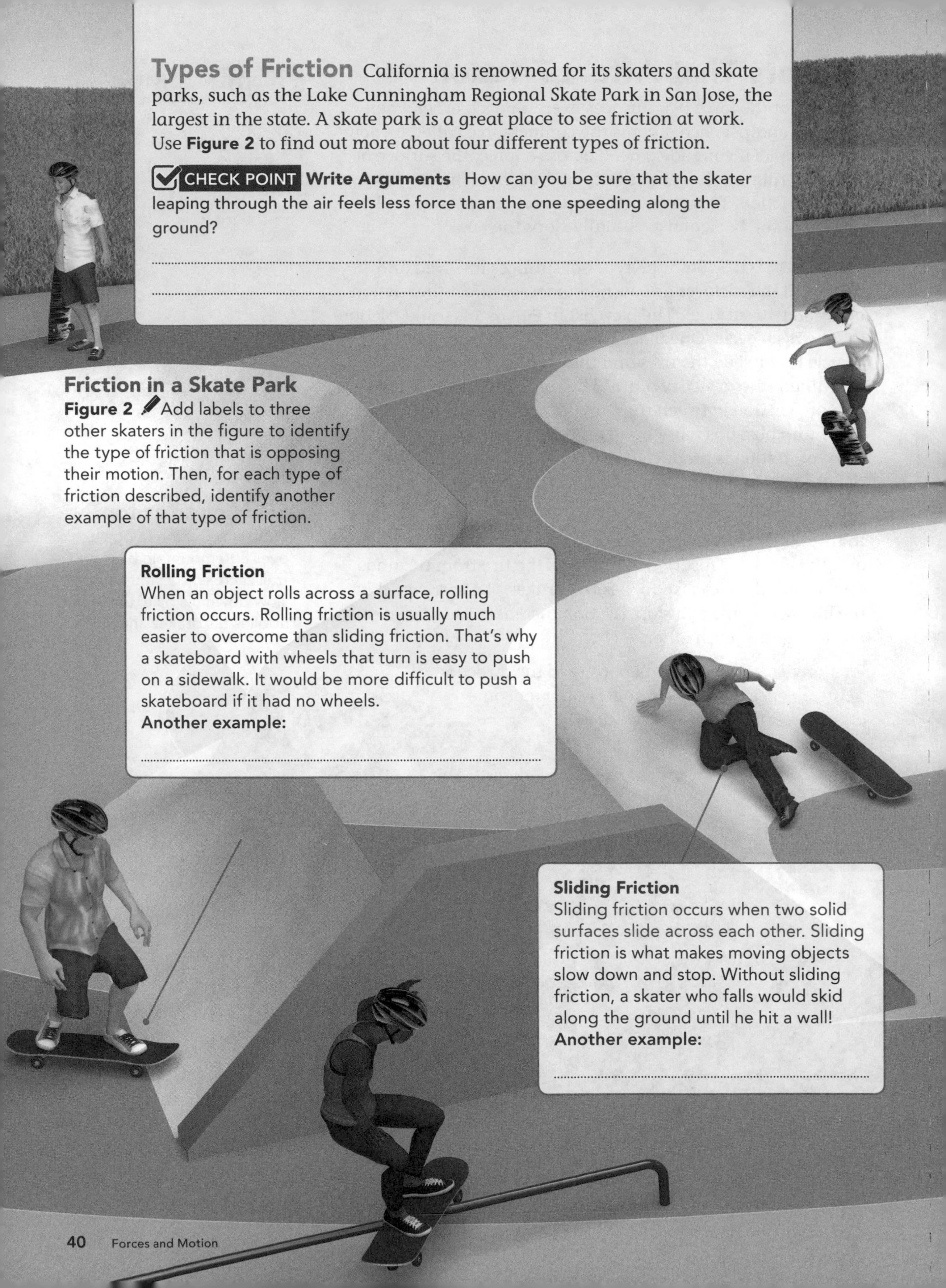

Rolling Friction
When an object rolls across a surface, rolling friction occurs. Rolling friction is usually much easier to overcome than sliding friction. That's why a skateboard with wheels that turn is easy to push on a sidewalk. It would be more difficult to push a skateboard if it had no wheels.
Another example:

....

Sliding Friction
Sliding friction occurs when two solid surfaces slide across each other. Sliding friction is what makes moving objects slow down and stop. Without sliding friction, a skater who falls would skid along the ground until he hit a wall!
Another example:

....

HANDS-ON LAB

Investigate Explore how friction is affected by different surfaces, and investigate how the force of friction affects the motion of objects.

Static Friction
Static friction acts on objects when they are resting on a surface. The woman trying to push the ramp is experiencing the force of static friction. Think about trying to push a couch across the room. If you don't push hard enough, the couch won't move. The force that's keeping the couch from moving is static friction between the couch and the floor. If you get some friends to help you push hard enough to overcome static friction, the couch starts moving and there is no more static friction. At that point, there is sliding friction.
Another example:

Fluid Friction
Fluids, such as water and air, flow easily. Fluid friction occurs when a solid object moves through a fluid. Fluid friction from your contact with water acts on your body when you swim. It also acts on a skater's body when he does a trick in midair. When an object moves through the air, the fluid friction acting on the object is often referred to as air resistance. Fluid friction is typically easier to overcome than sliding friction.
Another example:

Universal Gravitation
Figure 3 How does the gravitational attraction between these people compare to the gravitational attraction between the people and Earth?

VIDEO

Watch the video to learn about friction and gravitational Interactions.

Factors That Affect Gravity

While friction is an example of a contact force, gravity is an example on a noncontact force. Remember that gravity is a force that pulls objects toward each other. How is gravity experienced on Earth? Any falling object, such as an apple dropping from a tree, is an example of gravity. We are so familiar with objects falling that we may not think much about why they fall. One person who thought about this was Sir Isaac Newton. He concluded that a force called gravity acts to pull objects straight down toward the center of Earth.

Universal Gravitation On Earth, gravity is the force that makes the jumpers in **Figure 3** fall toward the water. From empirical evidence, Newton concluded that Earth's gravity also attracts the moon. About 350 years ago, Newton made the logical connection that the sun's gravity keeps the planets in their orbits.

CHECK POINT
Summarize What is the law of universal gravitation? In what century was it discovered?

Newton's realization is now called the law of universal gravitation. This law states that the force of gravity acts between all objects in the universe that have mass. So, any two objects in the universe that have mass attract each other. You are attracted not only to Earth but also to your school desk, the other planets in the solar system, and the most distant star you can see. Earth and the objects around you are attracted to you as well. You can clearly see the gravitational effect of Earth on an object. However, you do not notice the attraction between objects on Earth because these forces are extremely small compared to the attraction between the objects and Earth itself.

Factors Affecting Gravity

What factors control the strength of the gravitational force between two objects? These factors are the mass of each object and the distance between them.

The more mass an object has, the greater the gravitational force between it and other objects. The sun has the greatest mass and the strongest gravity in the solar system. Earth and the other planets, therefore, orbit around the sun. Gravitational force also depends on the distance between the objects' centers. As distance increases, gravitational force decreases. What happens when you drop your cell phone? You see your cell phone fall to Earth because Earth and your cell phone are close together. If your cell phone were on the moon, Earth would not exert a visible gravitational attraction to it because Earth and the phone would be so far apart. The phone would be visibly attracted to the moon instead.

Weight and Mass

Mass is sometimes confused with weight. Mass is a measure of the amount of matter in an object. **Weight** is a measure of the force of gravity on an object. Since weight is a measure of force, the SI unit of weight is a newton (N). If you know the mass of an object in kilograms, you can calculate its weight on Earth using Newton's second law. The acceleration due to gravity at Earth's surface is 9.8 m/s^2. Using its mass, you can find the weight of the object.

Net force = Mass × **Acceleration**

When you stand on a bathroom scale, it displays your weight—the gravitational force that Earth is exerting on you. On Earth, 1 pound equals 4.45 newtons. If you could stand on the surface of Jupiter, which has a mass around 300 times the mass of Earth, your mass would remain the same, but your weight would increase. This is because the gravitational force exerted on you is greater on Jupiter than on Earth.

INTERACTIVITY

Investigate how gravity affects falling objects.

Literacy Connection

Write Arguments Write an argument supported by evidence that explains why the pencil and notebook resting on your desk are not being pulled together by the force of gravity between them.

Describing g-Forces

Figure 4 A lowercase g is used as the symbol for acceleration due to gravity at Earth's surface (9.8 m/s^2). This symbol is used in the field of space engineering, where acceleration is often measured in "g's." These Blue Angel jets are flying over San Francisco, California. Engineers who design these planes must take into account the forces and acceleration experienced by the pilots and planes.

LESSON 4 Check

MS-PS2-4, MS-PS3-2

1. **Synthesize Information** What is the difference between weight and mass?

2. **CCC Stability and Change** Snow has been lying on a mountainside. Suddenly, it starts to move down the mountain. Which types of friction are observed in this avalanche? Where does each type occur?

3. **Apply Scientific Reasoning** Give a real-life example of fluid friction.

4. **Explain Phenomena** A 4-kg ball is 2 cm away from one 1-kg ball and 6 cm away from another 1-kg ball. Use the relationships among the balls to describe two factors that affect gravity. Also explain why the balls do not move toward each other unless acted upon by another force.

5. **SEP Construct Explanations** Explain why moving a heavy box on a wheeled cart is easier than pushing it across the floor.

Quest CHECK-IN

In this lesson, you learned how different types of friction affect the movement of objects. You also learned about universal gravitation and how this scientific law applies to objects on Earth and elsewhere in the universe.

Evaluate How might friction affect the movement of bumper cars? What role does gravity play in how bumper cars move? How might you use these concepts to make bumper cars safer?

HANDS-ON LAB

Bumper Cars, Bumper Solutions

Go online to download the worksheet for this lab. Learn how friction and gravity affect vehicles on different surfaces. Then brainstorm how these factors influence the speed and direction of bumper cars.

Math Toolbox

Graphing Kinetic Energy

When a moving object collides with an obstacle, it may cause a certain amount of damage. It will cause even more damage if it is moving faster or if it has more mass. The kinetic energy of an object (the energy due to the object's motion) depends on both the mass and the speed of the object, but not necessarily in the same way. How, exactly, do the mass and speed of an object affect kinetic energy? You can use graphs to see this relationship.

In the following scenario, Michael and Manuel are studying kinetic energy by observing sleds slide down a snowy hill. First they push one sled at different speeds down the hill and record the kinetic energy and speed. Then they push sleds of different masses down the hill and record the kinetic energy and masses. They put together two tables of data as shown using generic units.

Kinetic Energy and Speed					
KE	1	4	9	16	25
Speed	1	2	3	4	5

Kinetic Energy and Mass					
KE	1	2	3	4	5
Mass	1	2	3	4	5

Analyze Data

1. **Construct Graphs** On a piece of graph paper, construct a graph of kinetic energy versus speed from the first data table.
2. **SEP Interpret Graphs** Interpret the shape of the graph.
3. **CCC Scale, Proportion, and Quantity** Explain what the graph shows about the relationship between kinetic energy and speed.
4. **Construct Graphs** On a piece of graph paper, construct a graph of kinetic energy versus mass from the second data table.
5. **SEP Interpret Graphs** Interpret the shape of the graph.
6. **CCC Scale, Proportion, and Quantity** Explain what the graph shows about the relationship between kinetic energy and mass.

Conclusion How do Michael and Manuel's data show the relationship between kinetic energy, mass, and speed? Given the graphs, what do you think would cause more damage in a collision: a faster object or a heavier object?

TOPIC 1 Review and Assess

MS-PS2-1, MS-PS2-2, MS-PS2-4

Evidence-Based Assessment

In 2005, NASA sent a robotic spacecraft called DART to a satellite that was orbiting Earth. DART was supposed to demonstrate that it could move around the satellite and communicate with it, without a human on board. The spacecraft was supposed to come close to the satellite without actually touching it.

Here is how the DART system works: The spacecraft's navigation system estimates its position and speed. Then, commands are sent to the thrusters to keep the spacecraft on its intended path. Force from the thrusters causes a change in motion. If the GPS system communicates incorrect navigation data to the spacecraft, then it will travel incorrectly and use up its fuel.

DART made it into space, but then its navigation system failed, providing incorrect data on its position and speed. This failure caused DART to bump into the satellite. The force of the collision changed the motion of the satellite. Luckily it remained in orbit around Earth, but the mission was deemed a failure. Though NASA has had many successes, the science and engineering work involved with space exploration is extremely complex, and sometimes even the best-planned projects fail.

The diagram below shows the relative positions of DART and the satellite before the collision.

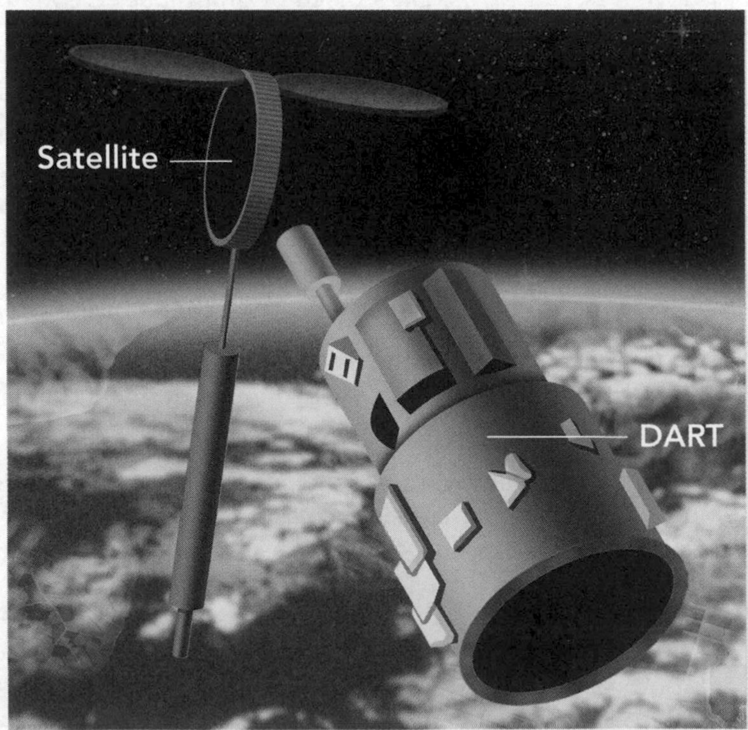

1. **Apply Scientific Reasoning** If the satellite had less mass, but the force of the collision was the same, then the collision would have
   A. caused the satellite to accelerate more quickly.
   B. caused the satellite to accelerate more slowly.
   C. caused the satellite to accelerate at the same rate.
   D. had no effect on the satellite's original motion.

2. **Cite Evidence** Complete the sentence.

   DART applied a(n) (balanced/unbalanced) force to the satellite during the collision, because ______

   a. both DART and the satellite had changed motion.
   b. the satellite was pushed and moved by DART.
   c. neither DART nor the satellite had changed motion.

3. **Draw Comparative Inferences** Select the answers that describe the action-reaction forces during the collision between DART and the satellite. Select all that apply.
   - ☐ The two forces are unequal in strength and opposite in direction.
   - ☐ The action force was the force of DART on the satellite.
   - ☐ The action force was the force of the satellite on DART.
   - ☐ The forces were balanced, so there was only an action force.
   - ☐ The reaction force was the force of the satellite on DART.

4. **CCC Scale, Proportion, and Quantity** Which do you think is stronger—the gravitational attraction between DART and Earth, or the gravitational attraction between DART and the satellite? Explain your answer.

5. **SEP Develop Models** What labels and symbols could you add to a picture to represent the forces acting on DART and the satellite during the collision? Describe what you would draw and write.

Quest FINDINGS

Complete the Quest!

Phenomenon Develop a multimedia presentation for your new bumper car design and the results of your testing. Be sure to include a logical argument of how Newton's third law of motion applies.

Synthesize Information Bumper cars have safety features to protect both the riders and the cars themselves. These features are built around how forces and the laws of motion affect the movement of the cars. What is another example of how forces and laws of motion affect your safety in your daily life?

INTERACTIVITY

Reflect on Your Bumper Car Solution

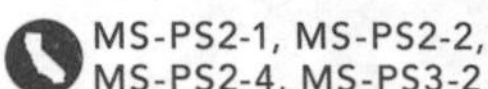

MS-PS2-1, MS-PS2-2, MS-PS2-4, MS-PS3-2

Stopping on a Dime

How can you **design** a **basketball court** so that players don't run into band members and other spectators near the court lines?

Background

Phenomenon Your school is hosting a championship basketball game, and the school band will be playing at the game. The band director wants the band to set up its instruments very close to the out-of-bounds line of the basketball court, so that the band will be front and center during the game. Some people at the school, however, have raised concerns about this plan. They feel that having band members so close to the court is unsafe because the members might be hit by players running off the court.

You and some of your fellow science students have been asked to design and conduct an experiment to determine whether or not the band director's plan is safe for both the band members and the players. In this experiment, you will investigate how time, distance, and average speed relate to changes in motion, and you will apply these concepts to the players on the basketball court.

Materials

(per group)

- tape measure
- 2 stopwatches or watches with second hands

Plan Your Investigation

To model the basketball players running off the court, you will determine the speed of someone running a distance of 10 meters. You will also determine how far it takes the runner to come to a complete stop after hitting the 10-meter mark. Discuss with your group how you will design and conduct the investigation. As you plan, consider the following questions with your group:

Demonstrate Go online for a downloadable worksheet of this lab.

- [ ] 1. What three properties of the players in motion do you need to consider?
- [ ] 2. What do you need to know to calculate the speed of a runner?
- [ ] 3. What tests will you perform?
- [ ] 4. How many trials of each test will you perform?
- [ ] 5. What type of data will you be collecting? Which variable is independent, and which is dependent? How will you collect, record, and organize your data?
- [ ] 6. What empirical evidence will you need to present after your investigation?
- [ ] 7. How will you present your evidence to communicate your results effectively?

Write your plan in the space provided on the next page. After getting your teacher's approval, conduct your investigation. Record the data you collect in your group data table.

Procedure

Data Table

Speed (m/s)

Stopping Distance (m)

Analyze and Interpret Data

1. **SEP Carry Out Investigations** Why was it important to carry out the steps of your procedure multiple times with each participant?

2. **CCC Stability and Change** How are unbalanced forces at work when a runner attempts to stop quickly after reaching the 10-m mark?

3. **SEP Interpret Data** Do your data seem reasonable for representing speeds and distances traveled by basketball players on a court? Explain why or why not.

4. **Provide Critique** Compare your procedure with the procedure of another group. What did that group do differently? What would you suggest to improve that group's procedure?

5. **SEP Construct Arguments** Write a proposal to the school that explains the importance of making sure the basketball court has enough space around it. In your proposal, suggest a strategy for making the court safer. Cite data from your investigation as evidence to support your points.

TOPIC 2

Energy

Investigative Phenomenon

How can you demonstrate that energy causes changes to occur?

MS-PS3-1 Construct and interpret graphical displays of data to describe the relationships of kinetic energy to the mass of an object and to the speed of an object.

MS-PS3-2 Develop a model to describe that when the arrangement of objects interacting at a distance changes, different amounts of potential energy are stored in the system.

HANDS-ON LAB

uConnect Explore how changes in energy can make a playing card jump.

How do we utilize energy in the form of liquid water?

What questions do you have about the phenomenon?

LESSON 1

Energy, Motion, and Force

Connect It!

Draw arrows on the photograph to represent the motion of the motorcycle.

SEP Construct Explanations The motorcycle needs energy to move. Where does the energy come from?

....

Write Explanatory Texts Describe how the rider exerts a force on the motorcycle.

....

....

Construct Explanations In what way do you think the motorcycle causes change?

....

Energy in Motion and Force

Explore forces and energy.

Energy is the ability to cause change. You cause change when you pick up your backpack. Motorcycles cause change during a race, as in **Figure 1**. The energy comes from fuel. As the fuel burns, it changes into other substances and releases energy.

Energy comes in many forms. Light, sound, and electricity are all forms of energy. Energy can also be transferred from place to place. For example, chemical energy is transferred from the food you eat to your body. Energy from the sun is transferred to Earth in the form of electromagnetic radiation. Energy is not something you can see directly. You can, however, observe its effects. When you touch something hot, you don't see the energy, but you feel the heat. You can hear the sound of a bass drum, but you can't see the sound energy itself. When you hold a magnetic near a pile of iron filings, you cannot see the magnetic field but you can observe the motion of the filings.

Reflect Think about the different methods you used to travel from one place to another today. In your science notebook, describe two of these ways. For each, identify the energy source that caused the movement.

Energy and Motion

It takes energy for motion to occur. An object is in motion if its position changes relative to another object. A pitched ball would not speed toward home plate without energy supplied by the pitcher. Energy supplied by food enables a racehorse to run around a track. Energy stored in gasoline allows the motorcycles in **Figure 1** to move at high speeds. In each of these examples, the more energy that is used, the faster the object can move.

Racing Around the Track

Figure 1 Energy, motion, and force are all involved in a motocross race at the Glen Helen circuit in Devore, California.

Energy and Force The relationship between energy and motion also involves forces. You can see many examples of this relationship on a construction site. Look at **Figure 2** and study the examples of how energy is used to apply a force that causes motion.

Explain How would you describe a force?

....

....

Force

Figure 2 When energy is used to apply force, objects can move.

CCC Energy and Matter Draw an arrow on each numbered picture to show the direction of the force being applied. Then label each arrow with "push" or "pull" to identify the type of force being applied.

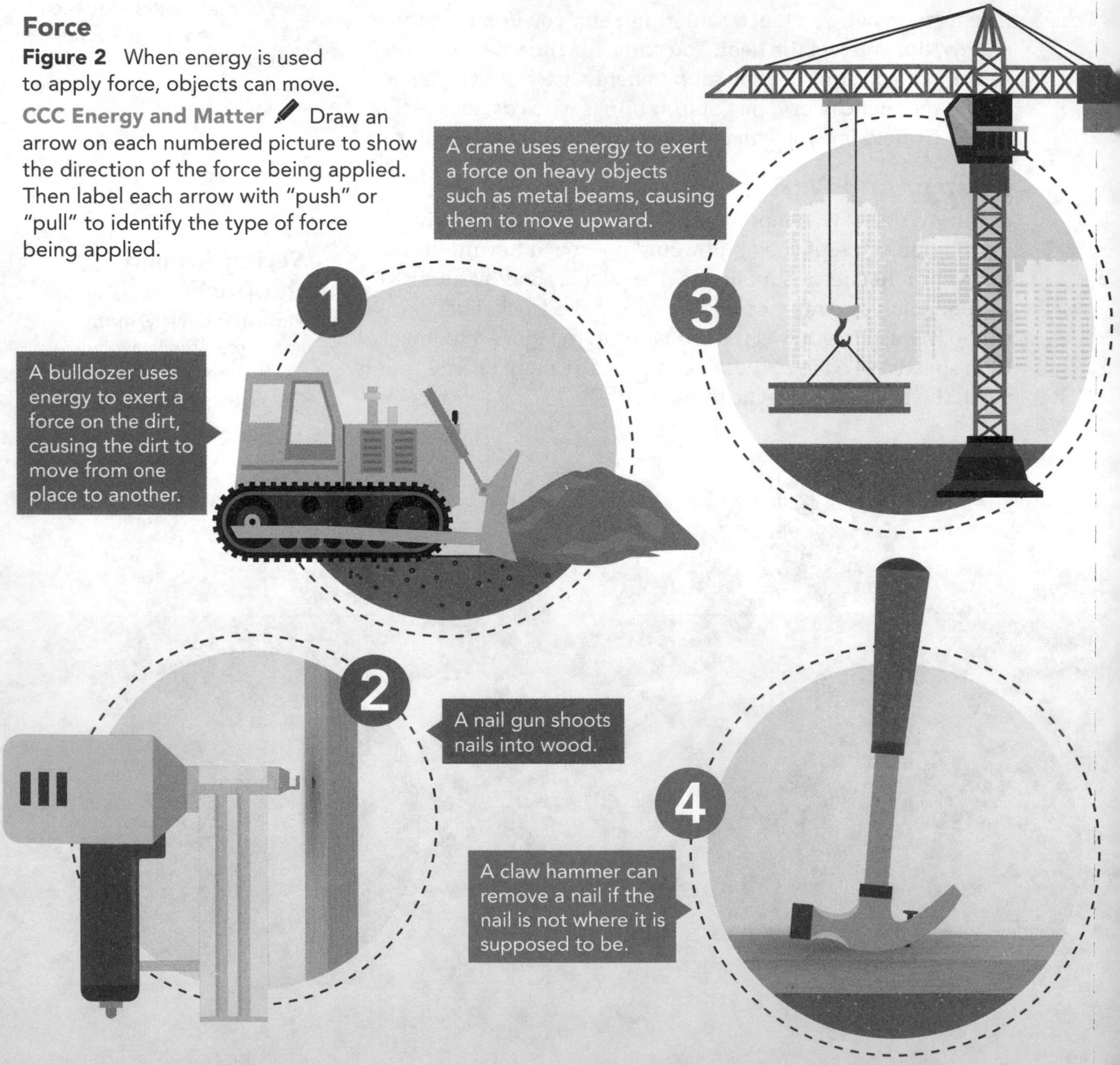

1 A bulldozer uses energy to exert a force on the dirt, causing the dirt to move from one place to another.

2 A nail gun shoots nails into wood.

3 A crane uses energy to exert a force on heavy objects such as metal beams, causing them to move upward.

4 A claw hammer can remove a nail if the nail is not where it is supposed to be.

LESSON 1 Check

1. **Explain** How are energy and motion related?

2. **Distinguish Relationships** How does energy relate to force?

3. **Apply Concepts** Give an example in which energy produces a force that causes motion.

4. **SEP Engage in Argument** Will a ball move faster if it is kicked hard or rolled gently?

LESSON 2

Kinetic Energy and Potential Energy

HANDS-ON LAB

uInvestigate Use a skateboard to model changes in kinetic energy.

MS-PS3-1 Construct and interpret graphical displays of data to describe the relationships of kinetic energy to the mass of an object and to the speed of an object.
MS-PS3-2 Develop a model to describe that when the arrangement of objects interacting at a distance changes, different amounts of potential energy are stored in the system.

Connect It!

Draw an arrow on the image to show the direction that you think the rocks and dirt are moving.

SEP Construct Explanations It takes a lot of energy to move this amount of dirt and rocks. What do you think is the source of this energy?

....

....

Apply Scientific Reasoning What is another example of something that starts moving suddenly?

....

....

Kinetic Energy

Study the landslide shown in **Figure 1**. In this image, dirt and rocks are moving rapidly down the side of the hill. As you read in Lesson 1, it takes energy to cause the motion you see in this photo. When objects are in motion, they are demonstrating a certain kind of energy—kinetic energy. **Kinetic energy** is the energy that an object possesses by **virtue** of being in motion.

Examples of kinetic energy are all around us. A car moving down a road exhibits kinetic energy. So does a runner participating in a race. As you sit at your desk in school, you exhibit kinetic energy every time you turn a page in a book or type on a keyboard.

Factors Affecting Kinetic Energy The kinetic energy of an object depends on both its speed and its mass. The faster an object moves, the more kinetic energy it has. For example, if a tennis ball moves at great speed, it has more kinetic energy than if the ball had been softly lobbed over the net. Kinetic energy also increases as mass increases. A wheel-barrow full of dirt has more kinetic energy than an empty wheelbarrow has, due to its greater mass.

INTERACTIVITY

Interpret graphs to understand the relationships among a snowboarder's kinetic energy, mass, and speed.

Academic Vocabulary

The phrase *by virtue of* means "because of." In what other way have you heard the term *virtue* used?

....

....

....

Landslide!

Figure 1 A landslide is a sudden movement of rock and soil. Landslides are common in many areas of California. Before the landslide, all the rocks and soil were in place and not moving.

VIRTUAL LAB

Complete a virtual lab online about skateboards.

Potential Energy

Potential energy is stored energy based on position or shape of an object. There are different types of potential energy. One of these types is **gravitational potential energy**. This type of potential energy is related to an object's vertical position—how high it is above the ground. The potential energy is stored as a result of the gravitational pull of Earth on the object.

HANDS-ON LAB

Investigate Develop a model with magnets to show how the arrangement of objects affects potential energy.

Very simply, the gravitational potential energy of an object becomes larger the higher it is above the ground. Suppose a bookcase has books on different shelves. The books on the higher shelves have more gravitational potential energy. If they were to fall off the bookcase, they would be moving faster just before they hit the ground. That is because the gravitational potential energy would have become kinetic energy.

The energy of the cyclist at the top of the hill shown in **Figure 2** is another example of gravitational potential energy.

Gravitational Potential Energy

Figure 2 A cyclist sitting still at the top of a hill displays gravitational potential energy. What makes it possible for the cyclist to have this type of energy?

....

....

....

....

Elastic Potential Energy Sometimes, an object has a different type of potential energy due to its shape. **Elastic potential energy** is the energy associated with objects that can be compressed or stretched. This type of potential energy can be stored in such items as rubber bands, bungee cords, springs, and bows that shoot arrows.

Explore the potential energy of roller coasters.

Trampolines also store elastic potential energy. Take a look at **Figure 3**. When the girl presses down on the trampoline, the trampoline changes shape. The trampoline now has elastic potential energy. This stored energy is transferred from the trampoline to the girl, sending the girl upward. During this energy transfer, the elastic potential energy of the trampoline is transformed into different types of energy. It becomes kinetic energy of the girl's motion and gravitational potential energy that increases as the girl moves upward.

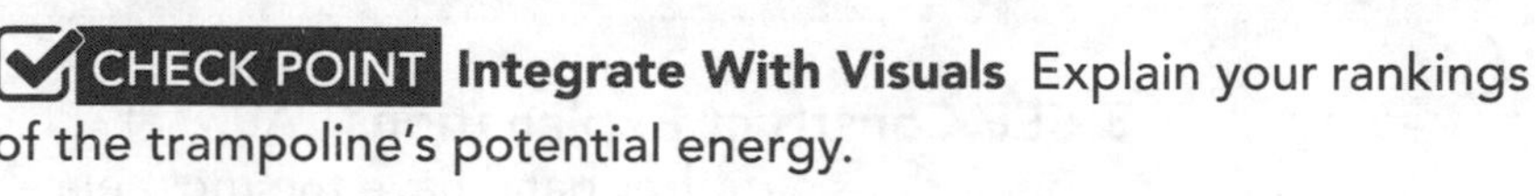

Integrate With Visuals Explain your rankings of the trampoline's potential energy.

....

....

....

Elastic Potential Energy

Figure 3 The energy stored in a stretched object, such as a trampoline, is elastic potential energy. Rank the amount of elastic potential energy of the trampoline from greatest to least using the words *most, medium* and *least*. Write your answers in the boxes next to the images.

LESSON 2 Check

1. **Explain Phenomena** Explain why a running deer has kinetic energy.

2. **Identify** What type of energy does a falling tree branch have?

3. **SEP Construct Explanations.** At what point does a rubber band have the most elastic potential energy? Explain.

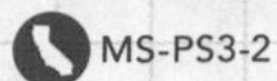

uEngineer It! Prototype to Product STEM

littleBits

MS-PS3-2

Prosthetics on the Move

INTERACTIVITY

Discover the properties of materials and changes in energy to guide your construction of a prosthetic limb.

How might you design a prosthetic arm that meets the needs of a modern, on-the-go person? You engineer it!

The Challenge: To design a prosthetic arm based on research into current prosthetic technology.

Phenomenon Until very recently, prosthetics, or artificial limbs, were made of wood, rubber, or plastic. These older prosthetics were solid and heavy, and they often made movement difficult.

When you walk, your foot muscles and leg muscles provide the force to push off the ground. The potential energy stored in your body becomes the kinetic energy of motion. Using an artificial leg, however, takes practice and can be uncomfortable because other muscles strain to carry the artificial limb.

Prosthetic design has advanced thanks to new technologies. In the early 2000s, engineers developed a carbon prosthetic for track athletes. This flexible leg bends and provides elastic potential energy to help the athlete run. The lighter weight of the materials allows the runner to move more efficiently with less muscle strain. Today, advanced engineers are working on limbs that are controlled by the electrical impulses in the human brain, mimicking the way our brains signal our muscles to move!

This prosthetic leg has the shape, weight, and flexibility to allow this runner to sprint again!

DESIGN CHALLENGE

How can you design and build a new kind of prosthetic limb? Go to the Engineering Design Notebook to find out!

LESSON 3

Energy Change and Conservation

Connect It!

Trace the movement of the surfer.

Infer How is the surfer able to soar through the air?

Energy Changes Form

All forms of energy can be transformed into other forms of energy. Energy can transform once (which we call a single transformation) or multiple times. A toaster provides a good example of a single transformation. Electrical energy passes through metal wires and is transformed into thermal energy.

If you eat toast, the resulting process is an example of multiple transformations. Your body transforms chemical energy stored in cells into the kinetic energy that moves your mouth. Your digestive system uses mechanical and chemical energy to digest the bread. Some of the chemical energy in the bread is released as thermal energy that helps your body maintain its temperature. Some of the remaining chemical energy is delivered back to your body's cells. The cells then transform that chemical energy into mechanical energy that allows your body to function.

Multiple transformations also go into the making of the bread. Sunlight, which is a form of electromagnetic radiation, is harnessed by wheat plants to create chemical energy. Mechanical energy is used to grind the wheat into flour. The flour is combined with water and yeast to make dough—more chemical energy. As the dough is baked in the oven, electrical energy is used to increase the thermal energy of the oven. Heat is transferred from the oven to the dough, and the thermal energy of the dough increases as it bakes into bread. Many of the processes that we rely on daily involve multiple transformations.

Literacy Connection

Cite Textual Evidence
What evidence in the text supports the claim that energy changes form? List two examples.

....

....

....

....

....

....

Dizzying Jumps

Figure 1 This surfer near San Clemente, California, uses his legs to jump up in the air. But most of the energy that allows him to travel through the air is supplied by something else.

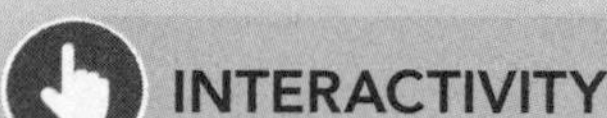

INTERACTIVITY

Explore different examples of energy transformations.

Energy Changes and the Law of Conservation

VIDEO

Look into the future and learn about hydrogen fuel cell cars and energy change and conservation.

There is a certain amount of energy in the universe, and we cannot make more of it or destroy any that already exists. Another way to state this idea is to say that energy is conserved. When one object loses energy, other objects must gain it. This is known as the **law of conservation of energy**. This law is a factor in both energy transfers and energy transformations. Energy either moves from one place to another or changes forms, but no energy is created or destroyed.

When a baseball is hit by a bat, as in **Figure 2**, the ball flies through the air. The law of conservation of energy explains why it does not keep flying forever, and why energy that is lost from the baseball is inevitably gained by something else. The kinetic energy of the ball transfers to the air and transforms into thermal energy due to the force of friction. The more air particles there are, the more transfer there is. So more kinetic energy transfers to the air when the air is dense. That's why baseballs travel farther and faster at a baseball stadium in Denver, Colorado, where the air is thinner, than they do in low-altitude ballparks where the air is denser.

Energy Is Conserved

Figure 2 After the ball is hit, it eventually slows down and falls. As it slows down, where does its kinetic energy go?

....

....

LESSON 3 Check

1. **Distinguish Relationships** What does it mean to say that energy is conserved in an energy transformation?

2. **SEP Evaluate Information** A train rumbles along the tracks at high speed. After it passes, the rail feels hot. What kind of energy transformation took place?

3. **SEP Engage in Argument** After a tornado moves through a forest, what kinds of evidence would there be of energy transformations or transfers?

4. **SEP Communicate Information** Explain the energy transformation that must occur for your body to participate in a physical activity, such as playing a sport.

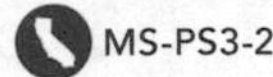

Evidence-Based Assessment

Darnell enters a design competition at school. The challenge is to construct a doorbell that works without electricity. The bell must ring loudly enough to be heard in another room of the house.

Darnell's idea is to use the bell, a ball, and gravity. A person would insert the ball into a hole in the wall. The ball would start from rest and fall a short distance to hit a bell. The ball would continue rolling back down and out to where the person could retrieve it in order to ring the bell again. Darnell draws a model of his doorbell design, as shown below.

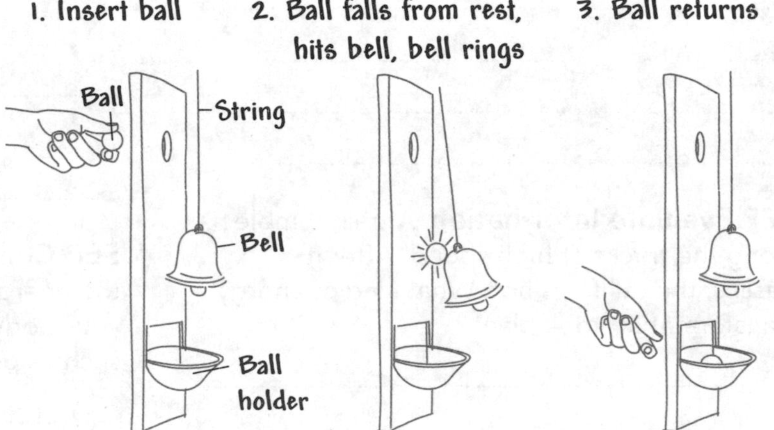

Darnell tests his design. For his first test, he uses a ping-pong ball, places the hole 1 meter above the ground, and hangs the bell 30 centimeters below the hole. He adds labels to his model to show how he set up his first test.

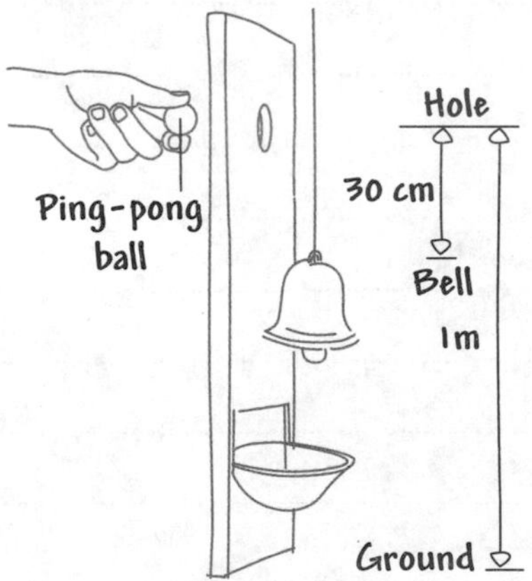

During this first test, Darnell finds that the bell does not ring loudly enough. Answer the following questions to help Darnell improve his design.

1. **CCC System Models** Which of the following two forms of energy are at play in Darnell's design?
   A. chemical energy and nuclear energy
   B. electromagnetic radiation and kinetic energy
   C. electrical energy and potential energy
   D. potential energy and kinetic energy

2. **CCC Cause and Effect** Based on the results of his first test, Darnell needs to modify his design to increase the loudness of the bell. Complete the table to help Darnell improve his model by predicting which change will cause a louder or softer ring.

Variable Changed	Outcome
Ball with less mass	
Ball with more mass	
Raise height of hole	
Lower height of hole	

3. **SEP Construct Explanations** What transfers and transformations of energy are occurring in Darnell's device? Select all that apply.
   - ☐ As the ball falls, kinetic energy transforms into potential energy.
   - ☐ Potential energy from the ball at rest transforms into kinetic energy as it falls.
   - ☐ Thermal energy from the air transforms into kinetic energy.
   - ☐ Kinetic energy transforms into thermal energy due to friction between the ball and air.
   - ☐ Kinetic energy from the ball is transferred to the ball holder when it lands.

4. **SEP Construct Explanations** How could Darnell change his materials or design so that the bell rings more loudly? Provide two options, and explain how they work.

MS-PS3-2

3, 2, 1 . . . Liftoff!

How can you **design** and build a **model** that explains the relationship between **potential and kinetic energy** in a rocket system?

Background

Phenomenon NASA is building a new website devoted to explaining the physics involved in launching rockets. They have asked you to help with a section of the website that deals with energy transfers and transformations. Your task is to design and build a model that explains the relationship between potential and kinetic energy in a rocket system.

Materials

(per group)

- scissors
- rubber bands
- meter stick
- marker
- metric ruler
- stapler
- cardboard tubes of varying diameters (from paper towels or wrapping paper)
- tape
- construction paper

Safety

Be sure to follow all safety guidelines provided by your teacher.

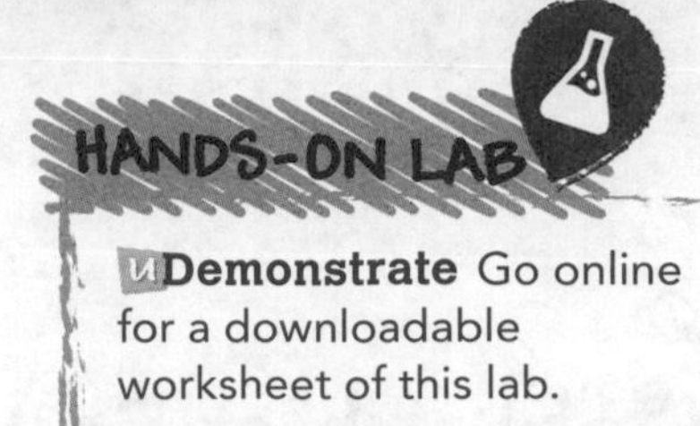

Demonstrate Go online for a downloadable worksheet of this lab.

Design a Model

☐ 1. Work with your group to develop a model of a rocket and launcher using the rubber bands, cardboard tubes, stapler, and other materials listed. Keep the following criteria in mind:

   A. Your rocket must be able to launch vertically into the air. As you work with your group, think about what each of the materials in your model will represent and how the model will operate.

   B. You will need to take at least three different measurements of how far the rubber band stretches and how far your rocket travels.

Plan Your Investigation

☐ 2. As a group, design an investigation to show that the amount of potential energy in the rocket launcher system affects the kinetic energy of the rocket.

As you plan your investigation, consider these questions. Write your ideas in the space below.

- How can you use the meter stick and the ruler in your investigation?
- What tests will you perform?
- How many trials of each test will you perform?
- What variables will you measure?
- What are the dependent and independent variables?

....

....

....

....

....

....

....

....

....

....

☐ 3. After getting approval from your teacher for your model design and procedure, conduct your experiment. Record the data in your table. See if you can discover a relationship between how far the rubber band stretches and how far the rocket travels.

Sketch of Rocket Launcher Model

Procedure

Data Table

Distance Traveled by Rocket (cm)				
Rubber band stretch (cm)	Trial 1	Trial 2	Trial 3	Average

Analyze and Interpret Data

1. **Analyze Structures** Describe how your rocket launcher works. What might you do to improve it if you could do this experiment again?

2. **CCC Patterns** What is the relationship between the amount of potential energy in the rocket launcher system and the kinetic energy of the rocket? Explain.

3. **CCC Systems** What transfers of energy did you observe in the rocket launcher system? What transformation of energy did you observe? Remember to consider gravity in your answer.

4. **SEP Engage in Argument** Use evidence from your investigation to support the argument that energy is being transferred and transformed throughout the rocket's travel. Draw a diagram that shows the rocket traveling upward, with different stages (on the ground, midway up, at its peak, and on its way down). Use labels to describe what is happening to the potential and kinetic energy at each stage. Label the position of maximum kinetic energy and the position of maximum potential energy.

Case Study

MS-PS2-2

FINDING YOUR WAY WITH GPS

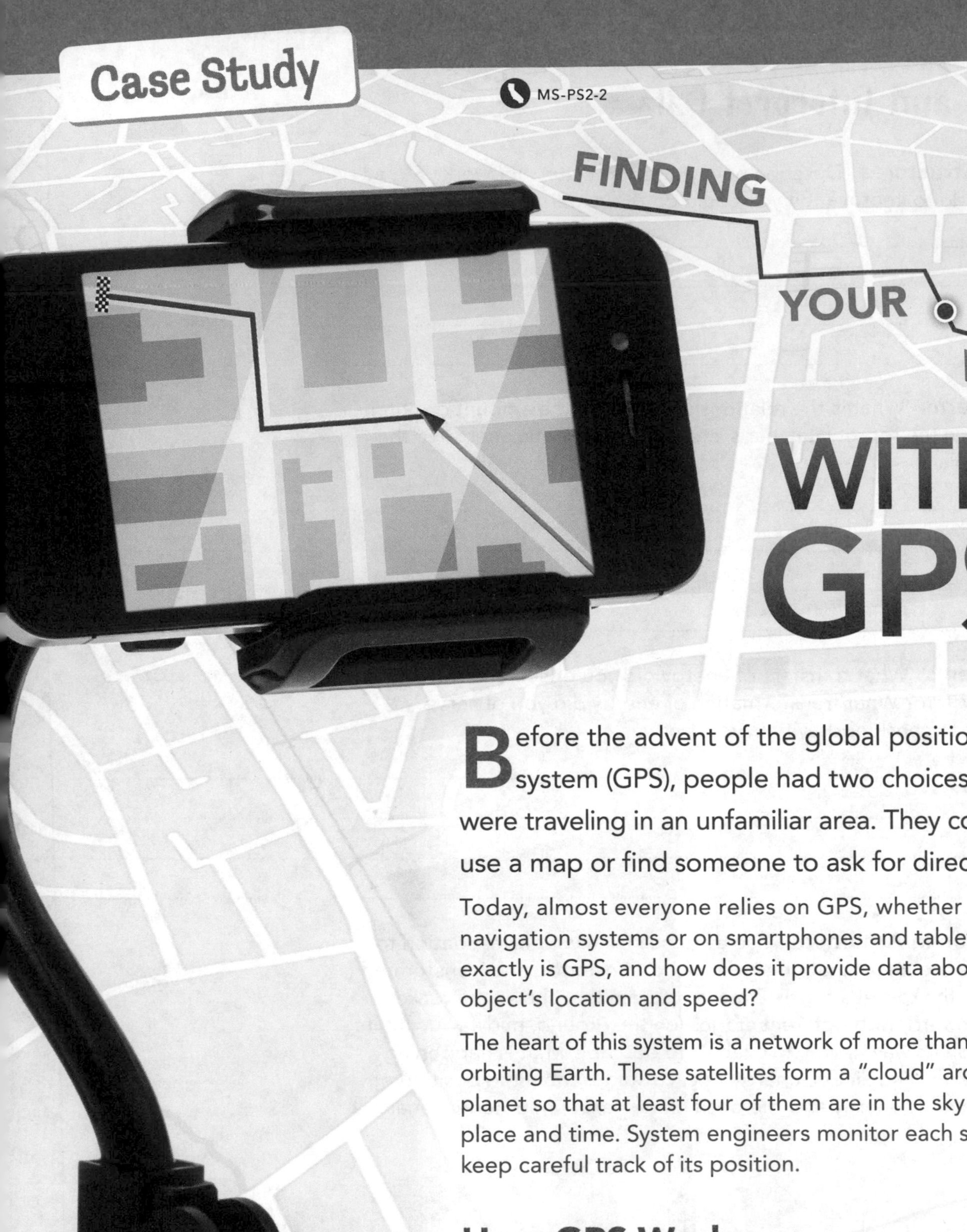

Before the advent of the global positioning system (GPS), people had two choices if they were traveling in an unfamiliar area. They could either use a map or find someone to ask for directions.

Today, almost everyone relies on GPS, whether in car navigation systems or on smartphones and tablets. But what exactly is GPS, and how does it provide data about a moving object's location and speed?

The heart of this system is a network of more than 24 satellites orbiting Earth. These satellites form a "cloud" around the planet so that at least four of them are in the sky at any given place and time. System engineers monitor each satellite to keep careful track of its position.

How GPS Works

Nearby satellites send radio signals to the GPS device, and the device calculates its position based on its distance from those satellites. Four satellites are needed for a GPS to calculate its latitude, longitude, and altitude with accuracy. If fewer satellites are used, only a relative position of the GPS device can be determined, not an exact location.

How GPS WORKS

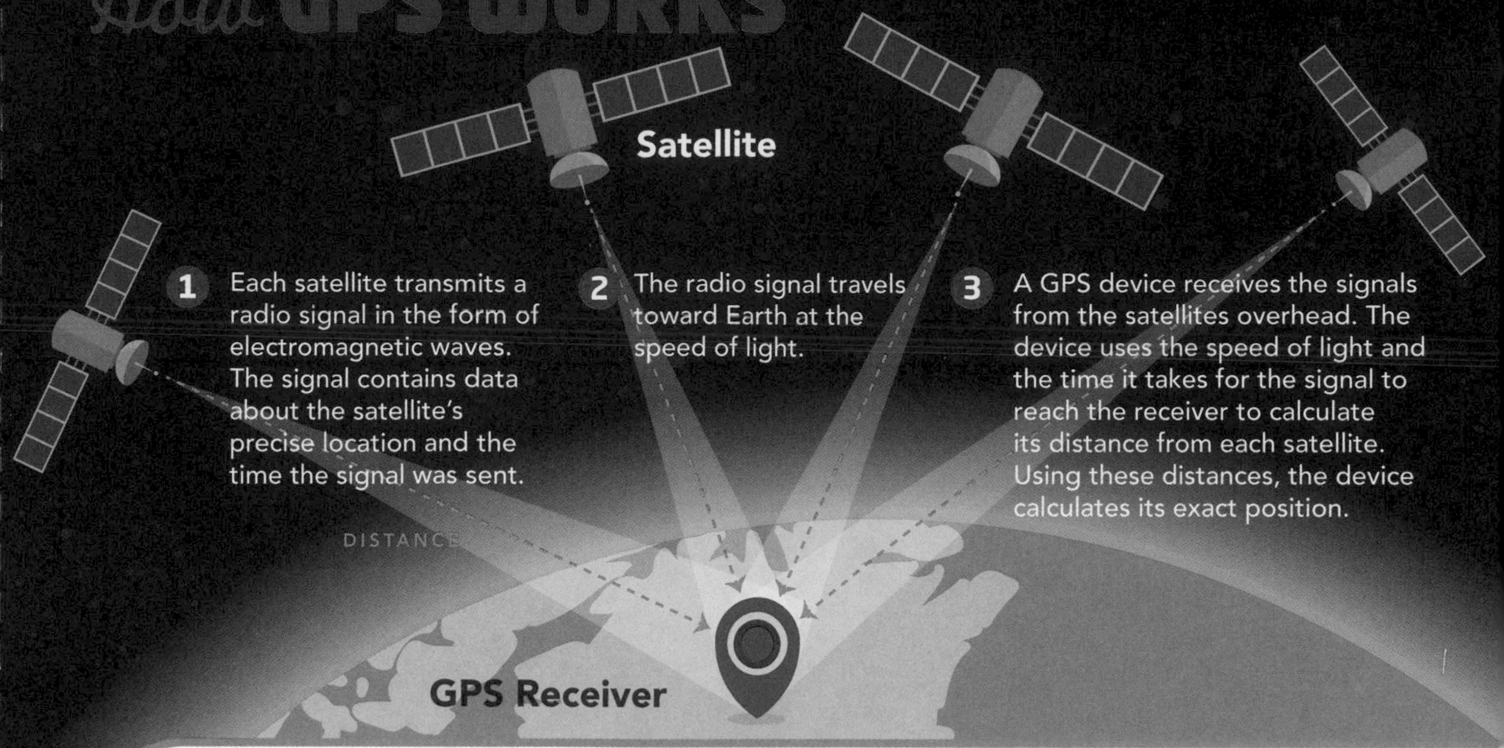

Satellite

1 Each satellite transmits a radio signal in the form of electromagnetic waves. The signal contains data about the satellite's precise location and the time the signal was sent.

2 The radio signal travels toward Earth at the speed of light.

3 A GPS device receives the signals from the satellites overhead. The device uses the speed of light and the time it takes for the signal to reach the receiver to calculate its distance from each satellite. Using these distances, the device calculates its exact position.

DISTANCE

GPS Receiver

Use the text and the diagram to answer the following questions.

1. SEP Use Models How does the GPS determine its distance from each satellite?

2. SEP Use Mathematics A radio signal from a GPS satellite takes only about 0.067 seconds to reach a GPS receiver. If the speed of light is about 300,000 km/s, then approximately how far away is the receiver from the satellite? Show your calculations.

3. CCC Systems and System Models Why is it necessary for engineers to know the precise location of each GPS satellite in the system?

4. SEP Construct Explanations Explain how a GPS device can determine the speed at which it is moving. Provide a real-world example to support your response.

Take Notes

Use this space for recording notes and sketching out ideas.

Revisit the Anchoring Phenomenon

Conduct an Investigation

Evidence **Now that you have completed the topics in this segment, do the following tasks.**

Promote Collaborative Conversations With a partner, discuss what you have learned in this segment and how it relates to the study of near-Earth asteroids and avoiding potential impacts. Then, complete the graphic organizer to explain why some asteroids can be dangerous and how potential impacts might be avoided.

Potentially Hazardous Asteroids

Why impacts can be dangerous:	How potential impacts can be avoided:

Case Study Now you will investigate some of the real-world factors that must be taken into account when considering a deflection plan. Answer the following questions.

1. **SEP Construct Explanations** Why do some asteroids collide with Earth?

2. **CCC Scale, Proportion, and Quantity** How do Newton's laws of motion help explain why a massive asteroid causes more damage than a lighter object?

3. **SEP Use Mathematics** The asteroid Bennu is a near-Earth object with a mass of 6.0×10^{10} kg. It has the potential to strike Earth about two centuries from now. Scientists estimate that the asteroid would be accelerating at 334.2 m/s^2 when it reaches Earth. Use a calculator to calculate the force of impact from the asteroid.

Revisit the Anchoring Phenomenon

Communicate a Solution

Develop a Deflection Method

Choose one of your ideas from the graphic organizer you completed to develop into a plan or method for deflecting a potential collision with asteroid Bennu. As you consider a plan, keep the following questions in mind:

- What kinds of forces and energy are involved in altering the asteroid's path?
- Where is the best place to attempt to deflect the asteroid?
- How much time would it take to carry out the plan?
- What risks are involved, and how can they be minimized?

Once you have developed your idea, complete the diagram by making a model of your plan. Use labels to explain the plan's components. Use arrows or other symbols to indicate the forces at work and the energy involved. Note any risks on the diagram for the steps or stages of your plan, and indicate how you intend to deal with them.

SEP.1, SEP.8

The Meaning of Science

Science Skills

Science is a way of learning about the natural world. It involves asking questions, making predictions, and collecting information to see if the answer is right or wrong.

The table lists some of the skills that scientists use. You use some of these skills every day. For example, you may observe and evaluate your lunch options before choosing what to eat.

Reflect Think about a time you misplaced something and could not find it. Write a sentence defining the problem. What science skills could you use to solve the problem? Explain how you would use at least three of the skills in the table.

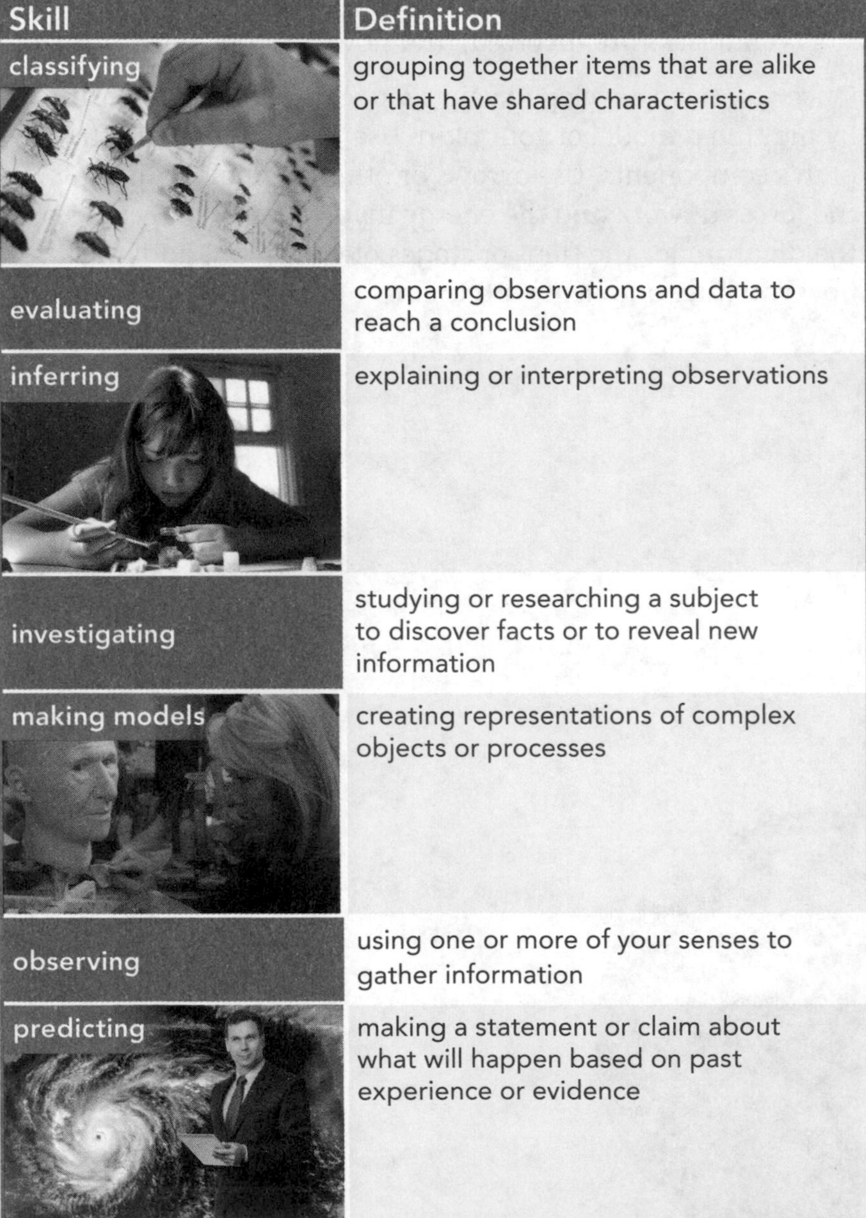

Skill	Definition
classifying	grouping together items that are alike or that have shared characteristics
evaluating	comparing observations and data to reach a conclusion
inferring	explaining or interpreting observations
investigating	studying or researching a subject to discover facts or to reveal new information
making models	creating representations of complex objects or processes
observing	using one or more of your senses to gather information
predicting	making a statement or claim about what will happen based on past experience or evidence

Scientific Attitudes

Curiosity often drives scientists to learn about the world around them. Creativity is useful for coming up with inventive ways to solve problems. Such qualities and attitudes, and the ability to keep an open mind, are essential for scientists.

When sharing results or findings, honesty and ethics are also essential. Ethics refers to rules for knowing right from wrong.

Being skeptical is also important. This means having doubts about things based on past experiences and evidence. Skepticism helps to prevent accepting data and results that may not be true.

Scientists must also avoid bias—likes or dislikes of people, ideas, or things. They must avoid experimental bias, which is a mistake that may make an experiment's preferred outcome more likely.

Make Meaning
Think about a bias the marine biologist in the photo could show that results in paying more or less attention to one kind of organism over others. Make a prediction about how that bias could affect the biologist's survey of the coral reef.

Scientific Reasoning

Scientific reasoning depends on being logical and objective. When you are objective, you use evidence and apply logic to draw conclusions. Being subjective means basing conclusions on personal feelings, biases, or opinions. Subjective reasoning can interfere with science and skew results. Objective reasoning helps scientists use observations to reach conclusions about the natural world.

Scientists use two types of objective reasoning: deductive and inductive. Deductive reasoning involves starting with a general idea or theory and applying it to a situation. For example, the theory of plate tectonics indicates that earthquakes happen mostly where tectonic plates meet. You could then draw the conclusion, or deduce, that California has many earthquakes because tectonic plates meet there.

In inductive reasoning, you make a generalization from a specific observation. When scientists collect data in an experiment and draw a conclusion based on that data, they use inductive reasoning. For example, if fertilizer causes one set of plants to grow faster than another, you might infer that the fertilizer promotes plant growth.

Write About It
Suppose it is raining when you go to sleep one night. When you wake up the next morning, you observe frozen puddles on the ground and icicles on tree branches. Use scientific reasoning to draw a conclusion about the air temperature outside. Support your conclusion using deductive or inductive reasoning.

SEP.1, SEP.2, SEP.3, SEP.4, CCC.4

Science Processes

Scientific Inquiry

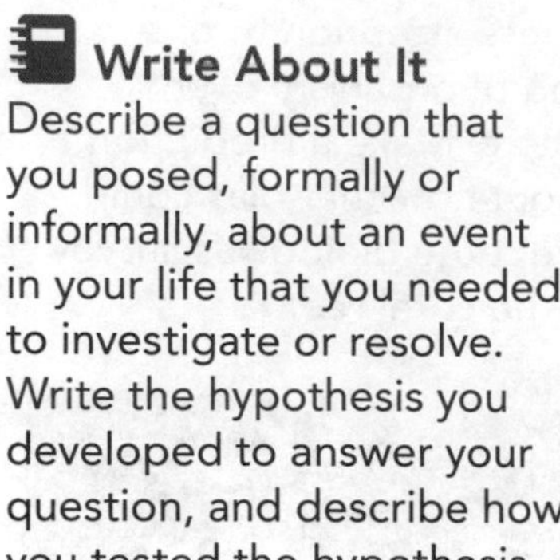

Write About It Describe a question that you posed, formally or informally, about an event in your life that you needed to investigate or resolve. Write the hypothesis you developed to answer your question, and describe how you tested the hypothesis.

Scientists contribute to scientific knowledge by conducting investigations and drawing conclusions. The process often begins with an observation that leads to a question, which is then followed by the development of a hypothesis. This is known as scientific inquiry.

One of the first steps in scientific inquiry is asking questions. However, it's important to make a question specific with a narrow focus so the investigation will not be too broad. A biologist may want to know all there is to know about wolves, for example. But a good, focused question for a specific inquiry might be "How many offspring does the average female wolf produce in her lifetime?"

A hypothesis is a possible answer to a scientific question. A hypothesis must be testable. For something to be testable, researchers must be able to carry out an investigation and gather evidence that will either support or disprove the hypothesis.

Scientific Models

Models are tools that scientists use to study phenomena indirectly. A model is any representation of an object or process. Illustrations, dioramas, globes, diagrams, computer programs, and mathematical equations are all examples of scientific models. For example, a diagram of Earth's crust and mantle can help you to picture layers deep below the surface and understand events such as volcanic eruptions.

Reflect Identify the benefits and limitations of using a plastic model of DNA, as shown here.

Models also allow scientists to represent objects that are either very large, such as our solar system, or very small, such as a molecule of DNA. Models can also represent processes that occur over a long period of time, such as the changes that have occurred throughout Earth's history.

Models are helpful, but they have limitations. Physical models are not made of the same materials as the objects they represent. Most models of complex objects or processes show only major parts, stages, or relationships. Many details are left out. Therefore, you may not be able to learn as much from models as you would through direct observation.

Science Experiments

An experiment or investigation must be well planned to produce valid results. In planning an experiment, you must identify the independent and dependent variables. You must also do as much as possible to remove the effects of other variables. A controlled experiment is one in which you test only one variable at a time.

For example, suppose you plan a controlled experiment to learn how the type of material affects the speed at which sound waves travel through it. The only variable that should change is the type of material. This way, if the speed of sound changes, you know that it is a result of a change in the material, not another variable such as the thickness of the material or the type of sound used.

You should also remove bias from any investigation. You may inadvertently introduce bias by selecting subjects you like and avoiding those you don't like. Scientists often conduct investigations by taking random samples to avoid ending up with biased results.

Once you plan your investigation and begin to collect data, it's important to record and organize the data. You may wish to use a graph to display and help you to interpret the data.

Write About It
List four ways you could communicate the results of a scientific study about the health of sea turtles in the Pacific Ocean.

Communicating is the sharing of ideas and results with others through writing and speaking. Communicating data and conclusions is a central part of science.

Scientists share knowledge, including new findings, theories, and techniques for collecting data. Conferences, journals, and websites help scientists to communicate with each other. Popular media, including newspapers, magazines, and social media sites, help scientists to share their knowledge with nonscientists. However, before the results of investigations are shared and published, other scientists should review the experiment for possible sources of error, such as bias and unsupported conclusions.

 SEP.1, SEP.6, SEP.7, SEP.8

Scientific Knowledge

Scientific Explanations

Suppose you learn that adult flamingos are pink because of the food they eat. This statement is a scientific explanation— it describes how something in nature works or explains why it happens. Scientists from different fields use methods such as researching information, designing experiments, and making models to form scientific explanations. Scientific explanations often result from many years of work and multiple investigations conducted by many scientists.

Write About It
Choose two fields of science that interest you. Describe a method used to develop scientific explanations in each field.

Scientific Theories and Laws

A scientific law is a statement that describes what you can expect to occur every time under a particular set of conditions. A scientific law describes an observed pattern in nature, but it does not attempt to explain it. For example, the law of superposition describes what you can expect to find in terms of the ages of layers of rock. Geologists use this observed pattern to determine the relative ages of sedimentary rock layers. But the law does not explain why the pattern occurs.

By contrast, a scientific theory is a well-tested explanation for a wide range of observations or experimental results. It provides details and describes causes of observed patterns. Something is elevated to a theory only when there is a large body of evidence that supports it. However, a scientific theory can be changed or overturned when new evidence is found.

SEP Construct Explanations Complete the table to compare and contrast a scientific theory and a scientific law.

	Scientific Theory	Scientific Law
Definition		
Does it attempt to explain a pattern observed in nature?		

Analyzing Scientific Explanations

To analyze scientific explanations that you hear on the news or read in a book such as this one, you need scientific literacy. Scientific literacy means understanding scientific terms and principles well enough to ask questions, evaluate information, and make decisions. Scientific reasoning gives you a process to apply. This includes looking for bias and errors in the research, evaluating data, and identifying faulty reasoning. For example, by evaluating how a survey was conducted, you may find a serious flaw in the researchers' methods.

Write About It
Suppose the conservation committee of a town wants to gauge residents' opinions about a proposal to stock the local ponds with fish every spring. The committee pays for a survey to appear on a web site that is popular with people who like to fish. The results of the survey show 78 people in favor of the proposal and two against it. Do you think the survey's results are valid? Explain.

Evidence and Opinions

The basis for scientific explanations is empirical evidence. Empirical evidence includes the data and observations that have been collected through scientific processes. Satellite images, photos, and maps of mountains and volcanoes are all examples of empirical evidence that support a scientific explanation about Earth's tectonic plates. Scientists look for patterns when they analyze this evidence. For example, they might see a pattern that mountains and volcanoes often occur near tectonic plate boundaries.

To evaluate scientific information, you must first distinguish between evidence and opinion. In science, evidence includes objective observations and conclusions that have been repeated. Evidence may or may not support a scientific claim. An opinion is a subjective idea that is formed from evidence, but it cannot be confirmed by evidence.

Make Meaning
Explain what empirical evidence the photograph reveals.

SEP.3, SEP.4

Tools of Science

Measurement

Making measurements using standard units is important in all fields of science. This allows scientists to repeat and reproduce other experiments, as well as to understand the precise meaning of the results of others. Scientists use a measurement system called the International System of Units, or SI.

For each type of measurement, there is a series of units that are greater or less than each other. The unit a scientist uses depends on what is being measured. For example, a geophysicist tracking the movements of tectonic plates may use centimeters, as plates tend to move small amounts each year. Meanwhile, a marine biologist might measure the movement of migrating bluefin tuna on the scale of kilometers.

Units for length, mass, volume, and density are based on powers of ten—a meter is equal to 100 centimeters or 1000 millimeters. Units of time do not follow that pattern. There are 60 seconds in a minute, 60 minutes in an hour, and 24 hours in a day. These units are based on patterns that humans perceived in nature. Units of temperature are based on scales that are set according to observations of nature. For example, 0°C is the temperature at which pure water freezes, and 100°C is the temperature at which it boils.

Write About It
Suppose you are planning an investigation in which you must measure the dimensions of several small mineral samples that fit in your hand. Which metric unit or units will you most likely use? Explain your answer.

Measurement	Metric units
Length or distance	meter (m), kilometer (km), centimeter (cm), millimeter (mm) 1 km = 1,000 m 1 cm = 10 mm 1 m = 100 cm
Mass	kilogram (kg), gram (g), milligram (mg) 1 kg = 1,000 g 1 g = 1,000 mg
Volume	cubic meter (m^3), cubic centimeter (cm^3) 1 m^3 = 1,000,000 cm^3
Density	kilogram per cubic meter (kg/m^3), gram per cubic centimeter (g/cm^3) 1,000 kg/m^3 = 1 g/cm^3
Temperature	degrees Celsius (°C), kelvin (K) 1°C = 273 K
Time	hour (h), minute (m), second (s)

Math Skills

Using numbers to collect and interpret data involves math skills that are essential in science. For example, you use math skills when you estimate the number of birds in an entire forest after counting the actual number of birds in ten trees.

Scientists evaluate measurements and estimates for their precision and accuracy. In science, an accurate measurement is very close to the actual value. Precise measurements are very close, or nearly equal, to each other. Reliable measurements are both accurate and precise. An imprecise value may be a sign of an error in data collection. This kind of anomalous data may be excluded to avoid skewing the data and harming the investigation.

Other math skills include performing specific calculations, such as finding the mean, or average, value in a data set. The mean can be calculated by adding up all of the values in the data set and then dividing that sum by the number of values.

Hour	Number of Ducks Observed at a Pond
1	12
2	10
3	2
4	14
5	13
6	10
7	11

SEP Use Mathematics The data table shows how many ducks were seen at a pond every hour over the course of seven hours. Is there a data point that seems anomalous? If so, cross out that data point. Then, calculate the mean number of ducks on the pond. Round the mean to the nearest whole number.

....

Graphs

Graphs help scientists to interpret data by helping them to find trends or patterns in the data. A line graph displays data that show how one variable (the dependent or outcome variable) changes in response to another (the independent or test variable). The slope and shape of a graph line can reveal patterns and help scientists to make predictions. For example, line graphs can help you to spot patterns of change over time.

Scientists use bar graphs to compare data across categories or subjects that may not affect each other. The heights of the bars make it easy to compare those quantities. A circle graph, also known as a pie chart, shows the proportions of different parts of a whole.

Write About It You and a friend record the distance you travel every 15 minutes on a one-hour bike trip. Your friend wants to display the data as a circle graph. Explain whether or not this is the best type of graph to display your data. If not, suggest another graph to use.

 SEP.1, SEP.2, SEP.3, SEP.6

The Engineering Design Process

Engineers are builders and problem solvers. Chemical engineers experiment with new fuels made from algae. Civil engineers design roadways and bridges. Bioengineers develop medical devices and prosthetics. The common trait among engineers is an ability to identify problems and design solutions to solve them. Engineers use a creative process that relies on scientific methods to help guide them from a concept or idea all the way to the final product.

Define the Problem

To identify or define a problem, different questions need to be asked: *What are the effects of the problem? What are the likely causes? What other factors could be involved?* Sometimes the obvious, immediate cause of a problem may be the result of another problem that may not be immediately apparent. For example, climate change results in different weather patterns, which in turn can affect organisms that live in certain habitats. So engineers must be aware of all the possible effects of potential solutions. Engineers must also take into account how well different solutions deal with the different causes of the problem.

Reflect Write about a problem that you encountered in your life that had both immediate, obvious causes as well as less-obvious and less-immediate ones.

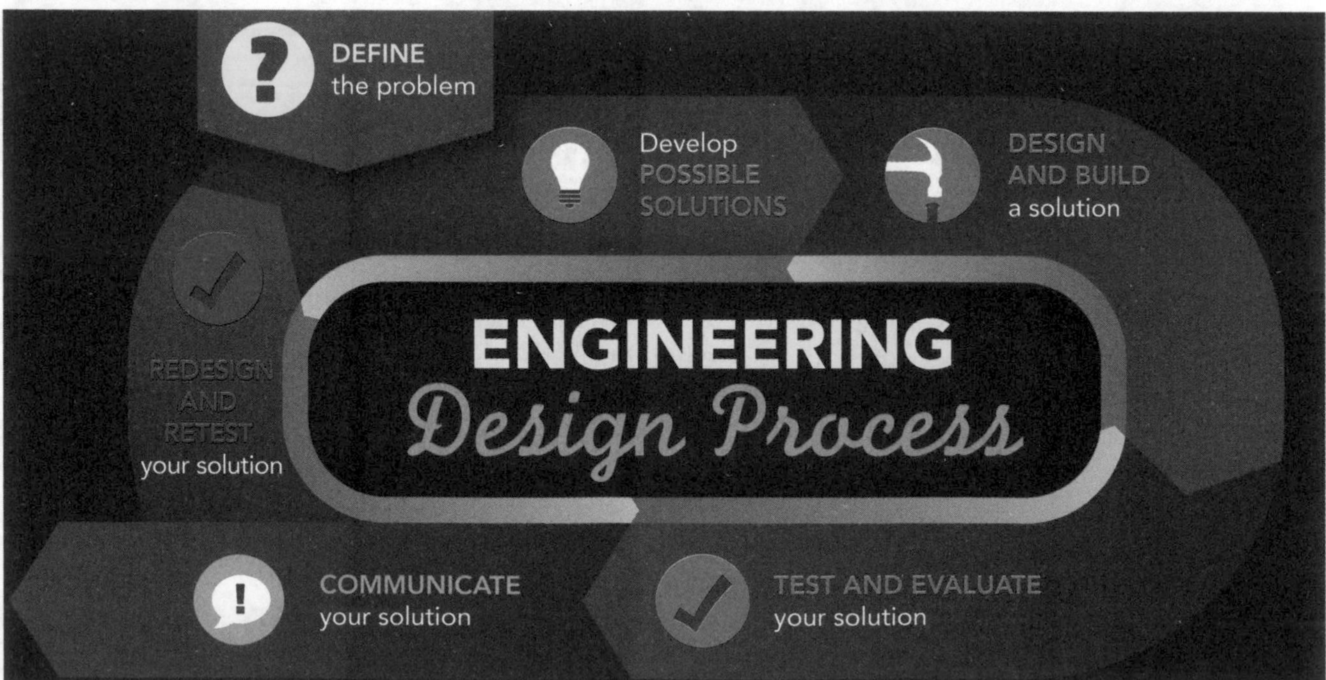

As engineers consider problems and design solutions, they must identify and categorize the criteria and constraints of the project.

Criteria are the factors that must be met or accomplished by the solution. For example, a gardener who wants to protect outdoor plants from deer and rabbits may say that the criteria for the solution are "plants are no longer eaten" and "plant growth is not inhibited in any way." The gardener then knows the plants cannot simply be sealed off from the environment, because the plants will not receive sunlight and water.

The same gardener will likely have constraints on his solution, such as budget for materials and time that is available for working on the project. By setting constraints, a solution can be designed that will be successful without introducing a new set of problems. No one wants to spend $500 on materials to protect $100 worth of tomatoes and cucumbers.

Develop Possible Solutions

After the problem has been identified, and the criteria and constraints identified, an engineer will consider possible solutions. This often involves working in teams with other engineers and designers to brainstorm ideas and research materials that can be used in the design.

It's important for engineers to think creatively and explore all potential solutions. If you wanted to design a bicycle that was safer and easier to ride than a traditional bicycle, then you would want more than just one or two solutions. Having multiple ideas to choose from increases the likelihood that you will develop a solution that meets the criteria and constraints. In addition, different ideas that result from brainstorming can often lead to new and better solutions to an existing problem.

Make Meaning
Using the example of a garden that is vulnerable to wild animals such as deer, make a list of likely constraints on an engineering solution to the problem you identified before. Determine if there are common traits among the constraints, and identify categories for them.

Design a Solution

Engineers then develop the idea that they feel best solves the problem. Once a solution has been chosen, engineers and designers get to work building a model or prototype of the solution. A model may involve sketching on paper or using computer software to construct a model of the solution. A prototype is a working model of the solution.

Building a model or prototype helps an engineer determine whether a solution meets the criteria and stays within the constraints. During this stage of the process, engineers must often deal with new problems and make any necessary adjustments to the model or prototype.

Test and Evaluate a Solution

Make Meaning Think about an aluminum beverage can. What would happen if the price or availability of aluminum changed so much that cans needed to be made of a new material? What would the criteria and constraints be on the development of a new can?

Whether testing a model or a prototype, engineers use scientific processes to evaluate their solutions. Multiple experiments, tests, or trials are conducted, data are evaluated, and results and analyses are communicated. New criteria or constraints may emerge as a result of testing. In most cases, a solution will require some refinement or revision, even if it has been through successful testing. Refining a solution is necessary if there are new constraints, such as less money or available materials. Additional testing may be done to ensure that a solution satisfies local, state, or federal laws or standards.

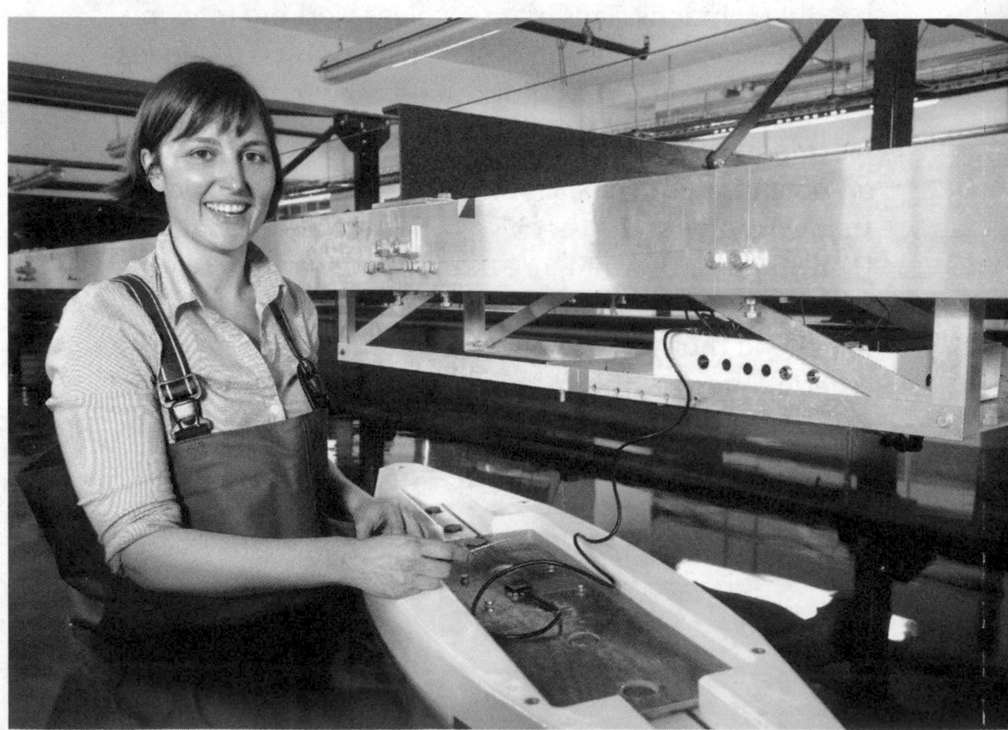

A naval architect sets up a model to test how the the hull's design responds to waves.

Communicate the Solution

Engineers need to communicate the final design to the people who will manufacture the product. This may include sketches, detailed drawings, computer simulations, and written text. Engineers often provide evidence that was collected during the testing stage. This evidence may include graphs and data tables that support the decisions made for the final design.

If there is feedback about the solution, then the engineers and designers must further refine the solution. This might involve making minor adjustments to the design, or it might mean bigger modifications to the design based on new criteria or constraints. Any changes in the design will require additional testing to make sure that the changes work as intended.

Redesign and Retest the Solution

At different steps in the engineering design process, a solution usually must be revised and retested. Many designs fail to work perfectly, even after models and prototypes are built, tested, and evaluated. Engineers must be ready to analyze new results and deal with any new problems that arise. Troubleshooting, or fixing design problems, allows engineers to adjust the design to improve on how well the solution meets the need.

SEP Design Solutions Suppose you are an engineer at an aerospace company. Your team is designing a rover to be used on a future NASA space mission. A family member doesn't understand why so much of your team's time is taken up with testing and retesting the rover design. What are three things you would tell your relative to explain why testing and retesting are so important to the engineering design process?

APPENDIX A

Safety Symbols

These symbols warn of possible dangers in the laboratory and remind you to work carefully.

Safety Goggles Wear safety goggles to protect your eyes in any activity involving chemicals, flames or heating, or glassware.

Lab Apron Wear a laboratory apron to protect your skin and clothing from damage.

Breakage Handle breakable materials, such as glassware, with care. Do not touch broken glassware.

Heat-Resistant Gloves Use an oven mitt or other hand protection when handling hot materials, such as hot plates or hot glassware.

Plastic Gloves Wear disposable plastic gloves when working with harmful chemicals and organisms. Keep your hands away from your face, and dispose of the gloves according to your teacher's instructions.

Heating Use a clamp or tongs to pick up hot glassware. Do not touch hot objects with your bare hands.

Flames Before you work with flames, tie back loose hair and clothing. Follow your teacher's instructions about lighting and extinguishing flames.

No Flames When using flammable materials, make sure there are no flames, sparks, or other exposed heat sources present.

Corrosive Chemical Avoid getting acid or other corrosive chemicals on your skin or clothing or in your eyes. Do not inhale the vapors. Wash your hands after the activity.

Poison Do not let any poisonous chemical come into contact with your skin, and do not inhale its vapors. Wash your hands when you are finished with the activity.

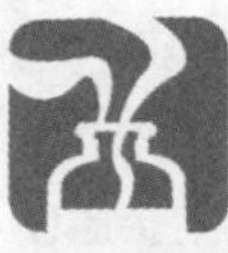

Fumes Work in a well-ventilated area when harmful vapors may be involved. Avoid inhaling vapors directly. Test an odor only when directed to do so by your teacher, and use a wafting motion to direct the vapor toward your nose.

Sharp Object Scissors, scalpels, knives, needles, pins, and tacks can cut your skin. Always direct a sharp edge or point away from yourself and others.

Animal Safety Treat live or preserved animals or animal parts with care to avoid harming the animals or yourself. Wash your hands when you are finished with the activity.

Plant Safety Handle plants only as directed by your teacher. If you are allergic to certain plants, tell your teacher; do not do an activity involving those plants. Avoid touching harmful plants such as poison ivy. Wash your hands when you are finished with the activity.

Electric Shock To avoid electric shock, never use electrical equipment around water, when the equipment is wet, or when your hands are wet. Be sure cords are untangled and cannot trip anyone. Unplug equipment not in use.

Physical Safety When an experiment involves physical activity, avoid injuring yourself or others. Alert your teacher if there is any reason you should not participate.

Disposal Dispose of chemicals and other laboratory materials safely. Follow the instructions from your teacher.

Hand Washing Wash your hands thoroughly when finished with an activity. Use soap and warm water. Rinse well.

General Safety Awareness When this symbol appears, follow the instructions provided. When you are asked to develop your own procedure in a lab, have your teacher approve your plan.

Take Notes

Use this space for recording notes and sketching out ideas.

GLOSSARY

A

absolute age The age of a rock given as the number of years since the rock formed.

absorption The transfer of energy from a wave to a material that it encounters.

acceleration The rate at which velocity changes.

acid rain Rain or another form of precipitation that is more acidic than normal, caused by the release of molecules of sulfur dioxide and nitrogen oxide into the air.

adaptation An inherited behavior or physical characteristic that helps an organism survive and reproduce in its environment.

amphibian A vertebrate whose body temperature is determined by the temperature of its environment, and that lives its early life in water and its adult life on land.

amplitude The height of a transverse wave from the center to a crest or trough.

analog signal A signal that allows for a continuous record of some kind of action.

artificial selection The process by which humans breed only those organisms with desired traits to produce the next generation; selective breeding.

asteroid One of the rocky objects revolving around the sun that is too small and numerous to be considered a planet.

astronomical unit A unit of distance equal to the average distance between Earth and the sun, about 150 million kilometers.

autosomal chromosomes The 22 pairs of chromosomes that are not sex chromosomes.

axis An imaginary line that passes through a planet's center and its north and south poles, about which the planet rotates.

B

bandwidth The amount of information that can be transmitted in bits per second.

birth rate The number of people born per 1,000 individuals for a certain period of time.

C

chromosome A threadlike structure within a cell's nucleus that contains DNA that is passed from one generation to the next.

clone An organism that is genetically identical to the organism from which it was produced.

comet A loose collection of ice and dust that orbits the sun, typically in a long, narrow orbit.

competition The struggle between organisms to survive as they attempt to use the same limited resources in the same place at the same time.

concave A mirror with a surface that curves inward or a lens that is thinner at the center than at the edges.

conductor A material that allows electric charges to flow.

conservation The practice of using less of a resource so that it can last longer.

constellation A pattern or grouping of stars that people imagine to represent a figure or object.

convex A mirror that curves outward or lens that is thicker in the center than at the edges.

D

death rate The number of deaths per 1,000 individuals in a certain period of time.

decibel (dB) A unit used to compare the loudness of different sounds.

deforestation The removal of forests to use the land for other reasons.

desertification The advance of desert-like conditions into areas that previously were fertile.

diffraction The bending or spreading of waves as they move around a barrier or pass through an opening.

diffuse reflection Reflection that occurs when parallel light rays hit an uneven surface and all reflect at different angles.

digital signal A signal that allows for a record of numerical values of an action at a set of continuous time intervals.

Doppler effect The change in frequency of a wave as its source moves in relation to an observer.

E

eclipse The partial or total blocking of one object in space by another.

elastic potential energy The energy associated with objects that can be compressed or stretched.

electric current The continuous flow of electrical charges through a material.

electric field The region around a charged object where the object's electric force is exerted on other charged objects.

electric force The force between charged objects.

electric motor A device that transforms electrical energy to mechanical energy.

electromagnet A magnet created by wrapping a coil of wire with a current running through it around a core of material that is easily magnetized.

electromagnetic induction The process of generating an electric current from the motion of a conductor through a magnetic field.

electromagnetic signal Information that is sent as a pattern of electromagnetic waves, such as visible light, microwaves, and radio waves.

electromagnetism The relationship between electricity and magnetism.

electron A tiny particle that moves around the outside of the nucleus of an atom.

electronic signal Information that is sent as a pattern in a controlled flow of current through a circuit.

ellipse An oval shape, which may be elongated or nearly circular; the shape of the planets' orbits.

embryo The young organism that develops from a zygote.

emissions Pollutants that are released into the air.

energy The ability to cause change.

equinox Either of the two days of the year on which neither hemisphere is tilted toward or away from the sun.

era One of the three long units of geologic time between the Precambrian and the present.

erosion The process by which water, ice, wind, or gravity moves weathered particles of rock and soil.

evolution Change over time; the process by which modern organisms have descended from ancient organisms.

exponential growth A rate of change that increases more and more rapidly over time.

extinct Term used to refer to a group of related organisms that has died out and has no living members.

F

fitness How well an organism can survive and reproduce in its environment.

focal point The point at which light rays parallel to the optical axis meet, after being reflected (or refracted) by a mirror (or lens).

force A push or pull exerted on an object.

fossil The preserved remains or traces of an organism that lived in the past.

fossil record All the fossils that have been discovered and what scientists have learned from them.

frequency The number of complete waves that pass a given point in a certain amount of time.

friction The force that two surfaces exert on each other when they rub against each other.

G

galaxy A huge group of single stars, star systems, star clusters, dust, and gas bound together by gravity.

galvanometer A device that uses an electromagnet to detect small amounts of current.

gene therapy The process of replacing an absent or faulty gene with a normal working gene to treat a disease or medical disorder.

generator A device that transforms mechanical energy into electrical energy.

genetic engineering The transfer of a gene from the DNA of one organism into another organism, in order to produce an organism with desired traits.

genome The complete set of genetic information that an organism carries in its DNA.

geocentric Term describing a model of the universe in which Earth is at the center of the revolving planets and stars.

geologic time scale A record of the geologic events and life forms in Earth's history.

gravitational potential energy The potential energy related to an object's vertical position.

gravity The attractive force between objects; the force that moves objects downhill.

H

heliocentric Term describing a model of the solar system in which Earth and the other planets revolve around the sun.

homologous structures Structures that are similar in different species and that have been inherited from a common ancestor.

GLOSSARY

I

inertia The tendency of an object to resist a change in motion.

information technology Computer and telecommunication hardware and software that store, transmit, receive, and manipulate information.

intensity The amount of energy per second carried through a unit area by a wave.

interference The interaction between waves that meet.

invertebrate An animal without a backbone.

K

kinetic energy Energy that an object possesses by virtue of being in motion.

L

law of conservation of energy The law that states that energy is conserved. When one object loses energy, other objects must gain it.

law of superposition The geologic principle that states that in horizontal layers of sedimentary rock, each layer is older than the layer above it and younger than the layer below it.

law of universal gravitation The scientific law that states that every object in the universe attracts every other object.

longitudinal wave A wave that moves the medium in a direction parallel to the direction in which the wave travels.

loudness The perception of the energy of a sound.

M

magnet Any material that attracts iron and materials that contain iron.

magnetic field The region around a magnet where the magnetic force is exerted.

magnetic force A force produced when magnetic poles interact.

magnetic pole The ends of a magnetic object, where the magnetic force is strongest.

magnetism The force of attraction or repulsion of magnetic materials.

mammal A vertebrate whose body temperature is regulated by its internal heat, and that has skin covered with hair or fur and glands that produce milk to feed its young.

mass extinction When many types of living things become extinct at the same time.

mechanical wave A wave that requires a medium through which to travel.

mechanism The natural process by which something takes place.

medium The material through which a wave travels.

meteor A streak of light in the sky produced by the burning of a meteoroid in Earth's atmosphere.

meteoroid A chunk of rock or dust in space, generally smaller than an asteroid.

moon A natural satellite that orbits a planet.

motion The state in which one object's distance from another is changing.

mutation Any change in the DNA of a gene or a chromosome.

N

natural resource Anything naturally occurring in the environment that humans use.

natural selection The process by which organisms that are best adapted to their environment are most likely to survive and reproduce.

net force The overall force on an object when all the individual forces acting on it are added together.

newton A unit of measure that equals the force required to accelerate 1 kilogram of mass at 1 meter per second per second.

noise Random signals from the environment that can alter the output of a signal.

nonpoint source A widely spread source of pollution that is difficult to link to a specific point of origin.

nonrenewable resource A natural resource that is not replaced in a useful time frame.

O

opaque A type of material that reflects or absorbs all of the light that strikes it.

orbit The path of an object as it revolves around another object in space.

overpopulation A condition in which the number of humans grows beyond what the available resources can support.

ozone A form of oxygen that has three oxygen atoms in each molecule instead of the usual two; toxic to organisms where it forms near Earth's surface.

P

penumbra The part of a shadow surrounding the darkest part.

period One of the units of geologic time into which geologists divide eras.

phase One of the different apparent shapes of the moon as seen from Earth.

pitch A description of how a sound is perceived as high or low.

pixel A small, uniform shape that is combined with other pixels to make a larger image.

planet An object that orbits a star, is large enough to have become rounded by its own gravity, and has cleared the area of its orbit.

point source A specific source of pollution that can be identified.

pollution Contamination of Earth's land, water, or air through the release of harmful substances into the environment.

potential energy Stored energy based on position or shape of an object.

protein Large organic molecule made of carbon, hydrogen, oxygen, nitrogen, and sometimes sulfur.

R

reference frame A place or object used for comparison to determine whether an object is in motion.

reflection The bouncing back of an object or a wave when it hits a surface through which it cannot pass.

refraction The bending of waves as they enter a new medium at an angle, caused by a change in speed.

relative age The age of a rock compared to the ages of other rocks.

renewable resource A resource that is either always available or is naturally replaced in a relatively short time.

reptile A vertebrate whose temperature is determined by the temperature of its environment, that has lungs and scaly skin, and that lays eggs on land.

resonance The increase in the amplitude of a vibration that occurs when external vibrations match an object's natural frequency.

revolution The movement of an object around another object.

rotation The spinning motion of a planet on its axis.

S

satellite An object that orbits a planet.

scientific theory A well-tested explanation for a wide range of observations or experimental results.

sediment Small, solid pieces of material that come from rocks or the remains of organisms; earth materials deposited by erosion.

sewage The water and human wastes that are washed down sinks, toilets, and showers.

sex chromosomes The pair of chromosomes carrying genes that determine whether a person is biologically male or female.

sex-linked gene A gene carried on a sex chromosome.

slope The steepness of a graph line; the ratio of the vertical change (the rise) to the horizontal change (the run).

software Programs that encode, decode, and interpret information.

solar system The system consisting of the sun and the planets and other objects that revolve around it.

solenoid A coil of wire with a current.

solstice Either of the two days of the year on which the sun reaches its greatest distance north or south of the equator.

species A group of similar organisms that can mate with each other and produce offspring that can also mate and reproduce.

speed The distance an object travels per unit of time.

standing wave A wave that appears to stand in one place, even though it is two waves interfering as they pass through each other.

star A ball of hot gas, primarily hydrogen and helium, that undergoes nuclear fusion.

GLOSSARY

static electricity A buildup of charges on an object.

sun A large, gaseous body at the center of the solar system.

sustainable Using a resource in ways that maintain it at a certain quality for a certain period of time.

sustainable use The practice of allowing renewable resources time to recover and replenish.

T

telescope An optical instrument that forms enlarged images of distant objects.

thermal pollution A type of pollution caused by factories and power plants releasing superheated water into bodies of water.

transformer A device that increases or decreases voltage, which often consists of two separate coils of insulated wires wrapped around an iron core.

transluscent A type of material that scatters light as it passes through.

transparent A type of material that transmits light without scattering it.

transverse wave A wave that moves the medium at right angles to the direction in which the wave travels.

U

umbra The darkest part of a shadow.

unconformity A gap in the geologic record that shows where rock layers have been lost due to erosion.

V

variation Any difference between individuals of the same species.

velocity Speed in a given direction.

vertebrate An animal with a backbone.

W

wave A disturbance that transfers energy from place to place.

wave pulse A pulse of energy that travels through an electric circuit when it is closed.

wavelength The distance between two corresponding parts of a wave, such as the distance between two crests.

weight A measure of the force of gravity acting on an object.

INDEX

Page numbers for charts, graphs, maps, and pictures are printed in italics.
Page numbers for definitions are printed in boldface.

A

B

C

D

E

F

G

INDEX

Page numbers for charts, graphs, maps, and pictures are printed in italics.
Page numbers for definitions are printed in boldface.

S

T

U

V

W

CREDITS

Photography

Photo locators denoted as follows: Top (T), Center (C), Bottom (B), Left (L), Right (R), Background (Bkgd)

Covers

Front: Tntemerson/iStock/Getty Images; Rafe Swan/Getty Images; Stefan Christmann/Getty Images; Dudarev Mikhail/Shutterstock; Sumiko Scott/Getty Images; Back: Marinello/DigitalVision Vectors/Getty Images

Instructional Segment 1

iv: Nick Lundgren/Shutterstock; vi: Joe McBride/Getty Images; vii: Josh Edelson/AFP/Getty Images; viiiT: Fabriziobalconi/Fotolia; viiiBkgd: Brian J. Skerry/National Geographic/Getty Images; ix: Dale Kolke/ZUMA Press/Newscom; 000: NASA Propulsion Laboratory/California Institute of Technology; 002: NASA Propulsion Laboratory/California Institute of Technology; 004: NASA Propulsion Laboratory/California Institute of Technology.; 005: NASA/JPL-Caltech; 006L: Mark Thiessen/National Geographic Magazines/Getty Images; 006R: NASA; 008: Joe McBride/Getty Images; 010: Heiner Heine/imageBROKER/Alamy Stock Photo; 012: Welcomia/Shutterstock; 014: Cassiohabib/Shutterstock; 015TR: Dmussman/IStock/Getty Images; 015TCR: Sonya Etchison/Fololia; 015CR: WilleeCole Photography/Shutterstock; 016BL: Gbh007/Getty Images; 016BR: Monkey Business Images/Shutterstock; 020: Mike Powell/Allsport/Getty Images; 022: Ron Bijlsma/ZUMAPRESS/Alamy Stock Photo; 023: Jim Zuckerman/Alamy Stock Photo; 024: Emma Yacomen/Alamy Stock Photo; 025: Heiner Heine/imageBROKER/Alamy Stock Photo; 028: WorldFoto/Alamy Stock Photo; 030TL: Hero Images/Alamy Stock Photo; 030CL: Janet Horton/Alamy Stock Photo; 031: ACnoncc/Alamy Stock Photo; 032: Omgimages/123RF; 033BL: Janet Horton/Alamy Stock Photo; 033C: Jiang Dao Hua/Shutterstock; 034: ImageBROKER/Alamy Stock Photo; 035TR: Full Image/Fotolia; 035B: Joe Haglage/Alamy Stock Photo; 036TCR: Barry Blackburn/Shutterstock; 036CR: ScofieldZa/Shutterstock; 038: Kuznetsov_Konsta/Fotolia; 042: Robert Daly/OJO Images/Getty Images; 043: Dinno Kovic/Southcreek/ZUMAPRESS/Alamy Stock Photo; 045B: Andrey Volodin/Alamy Stock Photo; 045CR: Koya979/Fotolia; 048: Jason O. Watson (Sports)/Alamy Stock Photo; 049: Gary Hamilton/Icon SMI/Icon Sport Media/Getty Images; 052: Josh Edelson/AFP/Getty Images; 054: Derek Watt/Alamy Stock Photo; 054: Rick Edwards ARPS/Alamy Stock Photo; 058: AFP/Getty Images; 060: Anatoliy Gleb/Fotolia; 063: Sportpoint/Fotolia; 064: Robert Beck /Sports Illustrated/Getty Images; 070: Stockbyte/Getty Images; 077: Science Source.